RUMORS OF POLAR BEARS

A full-length dramedy by
Jonathan Dorf

www.youthplays.com
info@youthplays.com
424-703-5315

 ISBN 978-1-62088-267-2.

CAST OF CHARACTERS

DEME, 18, female, survivalist meets teen next door.

ROMULUS, 15, male, Deme's brother, happy go lucky, a bit punk and sensitive all in one bundle.

ADAM, male, around Deme's age, punk meets beach meets Mad Max.

EVE, same age, Adam's girlfriend and not the sharpest tack.

SCRUBS, 13, hyperactive girl, something of a mascot like Anybodys from ***West Side Story***.

IKE, 18, male.

TINA, 18, female, Ike's girlfriend.

Inhabitants of New San Francisco

ANDI, 18, female, their leader, short for Andromeda.

CASSIE, 15, female, her younger sister, short for Cassandra, green meets punk.

DOC, 18, female, a self-styled "doctor."

Noah and Mrs. Middleton's Former Pre-K Drama Class

ECHO, an impish boy a little younger than Scrubs.

NOAH, around Deme's age, once a child prodigy musician, could be played by the actor who played Adam or Ike.

MERCURY, mid-teens, either gender, injured member of Mrs. Middleton's Former Pre-K class.

The Bikers

PAN, female, leader of a Mad Max-like gang of bikers terrorizing the West.

KALI, female, the consummate schemer and brains behind Pan.

TEEN CAPTIVE, female, though could be male.

Peoples of the First Nations

NANNURALUK, male, around Deme's age or slightly older, leader of the First Nations tribe.

KINGUYAKKI, female, Romulus' age and younger sister of Nannuraluk. Must be played by the actor who plays Cassie.

UGALIK, male, brother of Kinguyakki and on his way to becoming a shaman. Echo's age, he should be played by the same actor.

ENSEMBLE to play the inhabitants of New San Francisco (this group only must be all female), Mrs. Middleton's Former Pre-Kindergarten Drama Class, bikers, First Nations warriors, flexible in number but preferably 6-8 minimum, with no maximum.

Only Deme, Romulus and Scrubs appear in all three parts of the cycle, so productions wishing to limit cast size are encouraged to use multiple casting. Here is one possible cast:

DEME
ROMULUS
SCRUBS
ADAM/NOAH
EVE/KALI
IKE/NANNURALUK
TINA/PAN
ANDI/TEENAGE CAPTIVE
CASSIE/KINGUYAKKI
DOC/MERCURY
ECHO/UGALIK
ENSEMBLE

NOTES ON NAMES

Some names are fairly obvious in their pronunciations, but others not so much. To that end, below is pronunciation and origin information where I felt it might be useful:

DEME (DEM-ee) is short for Demeter.

ROMULUS (RAHM-u-luss) comes from the Roman myth. When shortened to Romey, however, it should be pronounced RO-mee (as in Romeo).

KALI (KAH-lee) is named for the Hindu goddess of death.

NANNURALUK (nah-noo-RAH-luke) is one of the names for "polar bear" in Inuit.

KINGUYAKKI (king-oo-YAH-kee) means "Northern Lights" in Inuit.

UGALIK (OO-gah-leek) means "arctic hare" in Inuit.

SETTING NOTES

Settings can be largely suggested, though the kiddie pool is necessary, and there likely should be at least a few selected set pieces that hint at the recycled nature of New San Francisco. In the Cambridge-Isanti production of the one-act (Act I), they constructed an elaborate city of recycled junk that hung in the air, whereas New San Francisco was entirely suggested in the Capital production. A good designer should feel free to go to town, as long as the set doesn't prevent the play from moving quickly.

The kiddie pool itself is most likely round and plastic, the kind that parents put in the yard for their small children—making it all the more ridiculous when the teens frolic in it.

PRODUCTION NOTES

In Act I, Scene 1, "freeway" may be replaced with "highway," depending on what suits your production. Likewise, it is not impossible for productions to substitute local examples for the geography used in the play, but great care should be taken to find examples that have the same sensibility. Thus, beginning in Act I, Scene 3, you may use something other than "New San Francisco," but try to find a word that is not only similar in meaning, but also in its musicality.

Similarly, in Act I, Scene 6, productions may substitute equivalent local examples for the Colorado River, California and Nevada, keeping in mind that in the original example, there really is considerable tension over this water. The line that refers to "mass evacuations of coastal regions" could be "shore regions" or "the flood plain" or something similarly appropriate if the location you're using is near a lake or river instead of an ocean.

It is important to avoid blackouts as much as possible between scenes.

Costumes should reflect the nature of the times: patched, dirty, mismatched and improvised. Mrs. Middleton's Former Pre-K class might wear clothing that is several sizes too small, while Noah's clothes might have been his father's, too big and patched and mended repeatedly. Except for the Inuits and the New San Franciscans and to a lesser extent the Bikers, nobody would be likely to have the ability to wash themselves and their clothes regularly, as they live on the road. Be particularly careful that footwear is appropriate; it's likely to be falling apart or "creative," if it exists at all.

ACKNOWLEDGEMENTS

The play premiered at Capital High School in Helena, Montana in May 2014 under the direction of Justin Olson with the following cast:

Deme – Jade Merriman

Romulus – Spencer Lamb

Scrubs – Bailly Noble

Adam, Pre-Kindergartener – Shane Adams

Eve, First Nation Warrior – April Kortz

Ike, Pre-Kindergartener – Zackary Heinze

Tina, Biker – Emily West

Andi – Kaitlynn Lindbo

Cassie/Kinguyakki – Paige Belstad

Doc, Pre-Kindergartener – Claire Peterson

Echo/Ugalik – Caleb Noble

Noah – Jackson Haddon

Mercury, Warrior, New San Franciscan – Mary Hartman

Pan – Adrianna Jones

Kali – Summer Diegel

Teenage Captive, New San Franciscan, Biker – Ali Barnicoat

Nannuraluk – Walker Lamb

New San Franciscan, Pre-Kindergartener, Warrior – Hannah Mondy

New San Franciscan, Pre-Kindergartener – Lena Tupper

New San Franciscan, Pre-Kindergartener – Julia Fisher

Biker, Warrior – Courtney Bawden

New San Franciscan, Biker - Lexi Brink-Woods

Stage Manager - David Jenks

Light Design/Assistant Director - Don Phillips

Assistant Director - Brenda Lamb

The original one-act version of ***Rumors of Polar Bears*** premiered at Cambridge-Isanti High School in Cambridge, Minnesota in May 2010 under the direction of Kelly Fairchild-Fahrni.

Special thanks to Jonathan Munoz-Proulx, who directed the first reading of the full-length play, and to Dr. Lawrence Kaplan of the Alaska Native Language Center at the University of Alaska Fairbanks, for his assistance with the Inuit language.

ACT I: OIL AND WATER

SCENE 1

(The near future. Somewhere in California, north of Los Angeles. DEME, 18, female, appears in a spotlight. Her clothes are survivalist meets teen next door, but it's better if the light can hit just her face. Her head is well-covered to shield it from the sun.)

DEME: I always wanted a baby polar bear. Its fur would be so white, I could hold it in my arms and rock it to sleep at night, and it would be soft and pure next to me. And each day we'd play games, the kind of games that parents and their baby polar bears play, and as it gets older it would know how to be. *(Beat.)* That's how it is with a lot of things. If we only got them when they were babies, maybe a lot of these things wouldn't have happened. And now the polar bears have gone far, far away. Or maybe they're just gone.

(Lights up to reveal Deme in a blighted landscape. Nearby, a squatter tent dwelling that has the feel of having been patched and mended repeatedly. ROMULUS, 15, enters. His clothing has the same survivalist streak, with a hint of punk in his boy next door wear. He has a bag slung over his shoulder.)

ROMULUS: Sun's down.

DEME: And?

ROMULUS: Friday night. *(Beat.)* Friday night!

DEME: Don't know how you even keep track.

ROMULUS: *(Singing it like a jingle:)* Friday night is party night. *(Points at his watch:)* It's magic. The magic watch that never stops.

DEME: It will.

ROMULUS: Sourpuss. *(Singing again:)* Friday night is party night. Make your work week come out right.

DEME: Speaking of work...

ROMULUS: Let's not speak of it. *(Once more singing:)* Friday night—

DEME: If you sing that one more time...

ROMULUS: You'll what.

DEME: Don't push me.

(Romulus pushes her super gently, just to be annoyingly literal.)

You know that's not what I meant.

ROMULUS: *(Singing:)* Friday night—

DEME: Don't—

ROMULUS: *(Continuing:)* is—

DEME: Romulus, I mean it.

ROMULUS: *(Beat.)* Here.

(He pulls a bunch of cans out of his bag.)

Tuna. Garbanzo beans. Creamed spinach. Creamed corn. Cream of wheat. Score or what?

DEME: You always do this.

ROMULUS: I didn't know cream of wheat came in a can. *(Beat.)* I always do what?

DEME: You always hold a few back until I'm mad, and then they pop out, peace offering.

(Romulus digs into his bag and pulls out one more can: peas.)

ROMULUS: I come in peas. *(Beat.)* Is it working?

(She hauls off as if to hit him. He flinches, but she runs her hand through his hair gently. Then she grabs his hair hard.)

Ow! I thought you liked peas.

(She kisses his hair and lets go.)

DEME: How many cans are left down there?

ROMULUS: Dunno. It's dark.

DEME: More or less.

ROMULUS: Less. Come on—it's Friday night. Can't we be all end of the world again on Monday? *(Beat.)* What?

DEME: That's such a Mom thing.

ROMULUS: Yeah? *(Beat.)* I think I remember less each day.

DEME: *(As their mom:)* Don't be all end of the world, Deme.

ROMULUS: I write in my book, but it just feels less and less real.

DEME: Dad had no sense of humor.

ROMULUS: I don't remember him at all.

DEME: You were three.

ROMULUS: Three should be good for something.

DEME: That was a crowded year.

ROMULUS: I hope he doesn't hate me for not remembering.

DEME: *(Beat.)* Why are we talking like this? It's Friday night. *(Singing:)* Friday night is party night.

ROMULUS AND DEME: Make your work week come out right.

ROMULUS: I'm goin' in head first this time.

DEME: Ha.

ROMULUS: One of these days I will. Dive bomber!

DEME: You ready?

ROMULUS: You got the stuff?

(Deme pulls a shoulder bag of her own from inside the squat.)

DEME: Do you have to ask?

(Romulus howls, as if sending a signal to distant friends. He's answered by cawing and barking and howling from elsewhere in the area.)

ROMULUS: To the party pool!

(Lights dim, except for the spotlight on Deme.)

DEME: The year Romulus turned three, I remember a man in a designer pin-striped suit and perfectly polished shoes swinging a sledgehammer at every inch of his Hummer, screaming that he would no longer be part of the problem. And when he's done, he sits on the curb and points at me to come closer and he says he wants to set it on fire, but he can't, because he just can't hurt the planet any more. He grabs my hand and starts to cry, and he says he's sorry he's crying, but he can't help it and isn't there some way he could give back the Hummer and the half hour showers for just one more minute with his wife? And then he stands up, wipes his face, tells me the Oil and Water Wars are all his fault, and throws himself onto the freeway below. *(Beat.)* I made that up. Not the Hummer or the hammer or the crying or him taking my hand or the freeway. But the Oil and Water Wars didn't start for another week, and that's just what we call them now because there's nobody to tell us different.

(The lights may go to black if absolutely necessary, but it would be better for them to crossfade and come up on the new location.)

SCENE 2

(Not far away, and not long afterward. A kiddie pool, empty of water, sits in an otherwise barren patch of ground. A nearby sign used to read "Danger: Keep Out," but danger has been crossed out, and the words "private club" scrawled in graffiti over top. Enter Deme and Romulus.)

ROMULUS: We're never first.

(ADAM, Deme's age and dressed in a sort of punk meets beach meets Mad Max chic, steps out of the shadows.)

ADAM: And you never will be.

(EVE, same age, his girlfriend and probably not the sharpest tack in the box, jumps out right after.)

EVE: Ambush!

DEME: You're just a regular Bonnie and Clyde.

ADAM: Adam and Eve, thank you very much, and we coulda' water whacked you no thing.

ROMULUS: But you gave the signal.

EVE: *(Mimicking him:)* But you gave the signal.

ADAM: Maybe we been waiting, watching for weeks, studying your ways...outlaws...

ROMULUS: Yeah, and maybe our parents are waiting for us at the spa.

EVE: What's a spa?

ADAM: Baby, it's not important.

EVE: I hate it when he uses words I don't know.

DEME: *(To Adam:)* You're right.

EVE: I'm a poet.

DEME: We shoulda been more careful.

ROMULUS: But—

DEME: Shut it.

EVE: *(Continuing her thought:)* Show some respect.

ADAM: Hey—we're here. It's all good.

DEME: Yeah, Eve. Give us one.

EVE: *(Beat.)* OK. *(Her poem:)*
Day hot sun dry hot
My favorite time is night
Pool of water wet!

DEME, ADAM AND ROMULUS: Amen.

EVE: Let's get this party started!

DEME: Where's Dare? And Tina and Ike?

(SCRUBS, the youngest at 13 or 14, bounds out of the bushes. She's the Anybodys of their world.)

SCRUBS: What about where's me? I call first into the party pool!

(Scrubs races out of her punk-Mad Max-tomgirl wear and into—considering the elements and dangers of exposure—a not quite bathing suit lickety split, jumping into the empty pool.)

ROMULUS: Hey—it's my turn.

SCRUBS: Party water!

(Romulus races to strip to a not quite bathing suit of his own.)

(Chanting:) Pour! Pour!

ROMULUS: Wait!

SCRUBS: Pour! Pour!

(Deme pulls a gallon jug out of her bag and pours its contents into the kiddie pool. The resulting "pool" is laughable: we're talking inches of water.)

Woohoo!

(Enter TINA and IKE, about the same age as Deme, Adam and Eve. They dress about the same, but with maybe just a bit more of a designer edge. They look gaunt.)

ROMULUS: That's enough, Scrubs. My turn now.

SCRUBS: Says who?

ROMULUS: Says me.

EVE: I says too.

DEME: *(To Ike and Tina:)* Where's Dare?

SCRUBS: I just started partyin'. *(Her party call:)* Rock on! Rock on hard!

(Scrubs jumps around and frolics as if this is the best thing ever.)

IKE: He's tired.

DEME: *(To Romulus:)* You gonna dive in?

ROMULUS: Maybe I will.

DEME: Romey says he's going to dive in.

(Adam tries to push his way past Romulus, but Romulus blocks him.)

ROMULUS: It's my turn.

ADAM: Not if I get there first.

DEME: Tina, you OK?

EVE: Ad, let him go.

(Adam and Romulus struggle playfully. Of course, just as Adam starts to get past Romulus, he has to stop to strip down to his swim gear, which gives Romulus time to block him again.)

ROMULUS: Not this week.

ADAM: *(Grabbing him again:)* I am the king of the party pool!

SCRUBS: Party, party!

EVE: Adam!

ADAM: I'm just havin' fun with him. *(Beat.)* Fine.

(Adam lets go of Romulus, then feints at him. Romulus flinches, but stands his ground.)

ROMULUS: Blow, Scrubs.

(Beat. Scrubs gets out. Romulus jumps in.)

Party, party!

ADAM, EVE, SCRUBS AND ROMULUS: Party, party! [etc.]

(Adam, Eve and Scrubs dance around the party pool, while Romulus frolics in it. Deme studies Ike and Tina, who looks longingly at the pool. Beat. Tina can't take it anymore and runs for the party pool, pushing the others out of the way and drinking from the pool.)

ROMULUS: Don't drink the party water.

ADAM: Yeah—if you drink it, what are we gonna party in?

(Tina stops drinking.)

TINA: Sorry. I was just really...thirsty.

DEME: Where's Dare?

EVE: Yeah. How we gonna party in the pool if you drink the water? Then we'd have to be sad all the time.

IKE: Dare's tired. He's lying down.

DEME: *(Beat.)* Is he lying down, Tina?

IKE: I just told you—

DEME: Tina?

(Beat. Tina shakes her head.)

Romey, get out of the water.

ROMULUS: But we're partyin'—

DEME: Get out of the water now!

(This time Romulus doesn't hesitate. He gets out and grabs his clothes. During this exchange, the others retreat ever so slightly from Ike and Tina. To Tina:)

Where's Dare?

TINA: We thought he just got too much sun—his skin had this splotch—

DEME: All over or in one place?

TINA: One place. Like a dot.

DEME: Like a bite?

TINA: I dunno. And then he got a fever and the sweats and more splotches and we kept givin' him water but it didn't help and then he...

DEME: We have to leave.

ROMULUS: Leave? Why?

EVE: Adam, what's going on?

DEME: Leave for good.

IKE: There's nothing wrong with us.

DEME: And Dare's just tired. Right, Ikey?

(Tina can't help herself. She drinks voraciously from the kiddie pool.)

SCRUBS: Tina, you're drinking the party water.

DEME: Show us your splotches.

IKE: We gave our part to Dare, that's all.

DEME: I bet you got 'em too.

(Until the end of the scene, Deme keeps her distance from Ike and Tina.)

IKE: Tina, stop it!

(Tina stops drinking again.)

DEME: We've gotta go.

ROMULUS: Where?

DEME: I don't know yet. North.

ROMULUS: Why do we have to go anywhere?

EVE: Yeah. We live here.

DEME: *(To Eve:)* Nobody says you have to go anywhere.

ROMULUS: So why do I?

ADAM: You can stay with us.

DEME: How long do you think you got?

EVE: Yeah. Stay with us.

DEME: How long 'til you get whatever they got?

ADAM: We go out there, we get water whacked for sure.

SCRUBS: I ain't gettin' water whacked.

DEME: For what? For our nothing?

ADAM: They won't know that.

DEME: There's no they. When's the last time we even heard a voice?

ROMULUS: *(Beat – indicating Ike and Tina:)* We can't just leave 'em here.

(Deme starts to pack. Beat. Romulus seethes, but he joins Deme in packing, getting road clothes, etc. Adam, Eve and Scrubs follow suit.)

DEME: And we didn't. *(Beat.)* I had a string from the place where the cans had almost run out.

(She lets the string go, and Ike grabs it. Deme begins to walk, and it unravels until it extends across the stage. Adam, Eve, Romulus and Scrubs walk near Deme, while Ike and Tina walk at the end of the string, with Ike holding it.)

That was how far they had to be. Romey wouldn't look at me for three days. But none of us caught what they had. And on the fourth day –

(Ike lets go of the string, and the lights fade on him and Tina.)

It could have been any of us. It could have been all of us. *(To Romulus:)* It could have been you.

ROMULUS: Don't expect me to say thanks. *(Beat.)* And now what?

DEME: We keep going.

ROMULUS: What's wrong with here?

DEME: Too hot.

ADAM: It's perfect.

EVE: Yeah. I love it.

DEME: It'll get worse.

ADAM: We're almost out of cans. We gotta restock.

DEME: From where? Got a better chance up north.

ADAM: Yeah—of runnin' out.

DEME: I heard buzzing last night.

ROMULUS: Every time you hear a bug now we move?

EVE: I don't think so.

SCRUBS: You don't even know that's what happened.

ROMULUS: Not for sure.

ADAM: *(Running at Eve:)* Bugggzzz... Bzzz...

EVE: *(Playing:)* Don't let it get me!

(Adam chases Eve. Scrubs joins in. Even Romulus gets into it, as they run all over the stage, with Romulus ultimately pantomiming a horrible death just as he looks up to realize that he's surrounded by TEENAGE GIRLS armed with makeshift weapons. Your production can use as many women as it likes, but there should be enough that the five characters already on stage appear to be in jeopardy.)

SCENE 3

(Very theatrically, perhaps even as a dance sequence – but more hip-hop/street/modern than ballet – the armed Teenage Girls break apart the group, prodding them in separate directions. One by one, they are whirled toward DOC, female, 18 or 19 and wearing a surgical-style mask and gloves, then returned to the middle – all except for Romulus, who disappears completely. Deme, Adam, Eve and Scrubs are left alone on stage.)

DEME: How long has it been? *(Beat.)* It's been too long. *(Beat – to the now vanished Teenage Girls:)* Hey! Why you takin' so long on him? *(Pause.)* Hey!

(A liquid-filled metal canister rolls onto the stage. They eye it suspiciously.)

SCRUBS: What is it?

DEME: Don't touch it.

SCRUBS: But what is it?

ADAM: Maybe it's a bomb.

EVE: Don't play.

ADAM: I'll protect you, baby.

SCRUBS: *(Poking at it very gently:)* It's squishy.

DEME: It's metal. *(Beat.)* I said hey!

SCRUBS: Maybe they killed him, and that's his blood.

(Deme leaps at Scrubs, who zips out of the way. Adam and Eve restrain Deme.)

ADAM: *(To Scrubs:)* You shut up. *(To Deme:)* Come on – you know she's just trouble with legs. *(Beat.)* You good?

DEME: As long as she stays over there.

(Adam and Eve let Deme go, though both stay close. Deme feints at Scrubs, who flinches and keeps her distance.)

ADAM: If everybody's too creepers to look, I'll do it.

EVE: Careful, baby!

(He gets in front of it. Studies it. Beat. He opens it, then gets down and sniffs.)

ADAM: Water.

DEME: Sure?

(Beat. He tips it toward his mouth.)

EVE: Adam!

(He sips.)

ADAM: Wet. Water.

EVE: They gave us water?

(Eve and Deme gather around for their drink, but Scrubs hangs back.)

DEME: Save some for Romey.

SCRUBS: *(Beat.)* What about me?

(Deme gives her a long look, then turns away.)

I miss the party pool.

(Deme steps out of the scene.)

DEME: Scrubs is—

(Scrubs walks into Deme's "out of time" moment.)

SCRUBS: I can talk about myself.

DEME: Scrubs has no sense of boundaries.

SCRUBS: So? *(Beat.)* Fine.

(Scrubs goes back into the scene.)

DEME: That's how she's been since we found her. Yeah, if she does the tellin', she'll leave out the part where she's a stick-thin carcass on the side of the road a few hours short of a prophet to send her home. But as cold as the body's goin', the eyes are fire. She shoulda been dead a week before we found her, but those eyes didn't believe they should close. *(Beat.)* Those eyes believe in the polar bears too. Even if sometimes I want to stick my fist so far up that big mouth it's gonna come out the back of her head and wave.

(The lights shift.)

Give her a sip. *(To Scrubs:)* But count to 100 in your head before you swallow it. Slow.

SCRUBS: But—

DEME: 100.

EVE: *(Sidling up to Deme:)* Do you get more out of it that way?

DEME: I just want her to shut up for a couple minutes.

(The lights fade on them and up on where Romulus stands alone. CASSIE, same age as Romulus and dressed in a green meets punk motif, as are most of the others of her settlement, watches him, cautious but compelled. A pair of Guards from the raiding party stand at a watchful distance.)

ANDI: *(Off:)* Don't go near him.

CASSIE: I'm not.

ROMULUS: Where's Deme?

ANDI: *(Off:)* You are.

ROMULUS: Where's my sister?

CASSIE: The other ones aren't broken. Why should he be?

(Doc, backpack slung over her shoulders, approaches.)

DOC: Only takes one. *(To Romulus:)* Turn out your pockets.

(Romulus obeys.)

ROMULUS: What are you doing?

DOC: I'm a doctor.

(She shoves a thermometer in his mouth.)

ROMULUS: There's nothing—

DOC: Don't talk.

CASSIE: He's fine.

DOC: *(To Cassie:)* Move back.

(She pulls the thermometer out of his mouth and checks it.)

ROMULUS: You can't be a doctor. You're my sister's age.

DOC: *(Meaning he's not sick:)* OK.

(Doc takes off her mask.)

Welcome to New San Francisco.

(Lights up on the rest of the stage—and the entirely recycled set of New San Francisco, which can be as elaborate or as suggested as your production needs. Deme, Adam, Eve and Scrubs are there, reunited with Romulus. Deme hugs him tight.)

SCRUBS: *(Looking around her:)* Rock on!

ROMULUS: I'm fine.

DEME: I didn't know what—

ROMULUS: I'm fine. *(Beat—not so harsh:)* I'm fine. Really.

(Deme nods.)

SCRUBS: Rock on hard...

DEME: New San Francisco.

ANDI: We started with nothing.

(Each New San Francisco Chorus line is meant to be said by a different individual, though it is possible for your production to experiment with having the same line said by multiple actors at once.)

NEW SAN FRANCISCO CHORUS: We love it here.
We like it.

ANDI: Everything is made out of something that was before.

NEW SAN FRANCISCO CHORUS: We have a stream.
We think it's clean.

ADAM: I smelled the water, and it doesn't smell.

NEW SAN FRANCISCO CHORUS: We boil it in case, but we think it's clean.

ANDI: We heat our water with the sun.

NEW SAN FRANCISCO CHORUS: Can't be too careful.
Not after what happened before.

CASSIE: Warm showers.

NEW SAN FRANCISCO CHORUS: A sauna.
We got a spa.

SCRUBS: Rock on.

NEW SAN FRANCISCO CHORUS: We have light here.
Cooking.
And a garden.
Steamed veggies.

ROMULUS: No more fishing in dark holes for cans.

EVE: New San Francisco.

ANDI: And it was good.

CASSIE: As good as it gets.

NEW SAN FRANCISCO CHORUS: Don't forget the windmill. Two next week.
Then three.
Our carbon footprint...

CASSIE: Invisible.

ANDI: Give more than we take.

EVE: New San Francisco.
Sun, wind, water—starting over.
Makes it feel like home.

NEW SAN FRANCISCO CHORUS: Some of the plants aren't as green as they were.
Some of the plants are turning brown.
There's not as much water as there was.
There's water on the other side of the mountains.
Salt water.
The other side of the mountains is underwater.
With water we can't drink.

ANDI: Water for the plants.

CASSIE: I see green again.

NEW SAN FRANCISCO CHORUS: Breathe again.
We can all breathe again.
Cassie sees it.
The visions.
They're never wrong. It'll all heal.

ADAM: I could get used to this, baby. Livin' the spa life.

EVE: Spa. Why is everybody so nutty about spa?

ADAM: Compared to before, this is heaven.

ANDI: You help, you can stay.

EVE: Tell me what spa is right now, or I'm gonna scream.

SCRUBS: I want to see me some plants.

FIRST TEEN GIRL: I'll show you.

SECOND TEEN GIRL: We garden.

ADAM: Spa is the most beautiful word in the world.

SCRUBS: Can I garden?

EVE: More beautiful than party pool?

FIRST TEEN GIRL: Rock on, girl.

SCRUBS: *(Recognizing a kindred spirit:)* Rock on!

(Scrubs exits with the First and Second Teen Girls.)

ADAM: Somebody take us to the spa.

EVE: To the spa!

(The Third and Fourth Teen Girl [or any others from the New San Francisco Chorus] escort Adam and Eve offstage.)

ROMULUS: I'll do something. We help we can stay, right?

ANDI: That's right.

ROMULUS: What you want me to do?

DEME: *(Sotto to Romulus:)* We're not staying.

ROMULUS: Why not?

ANDI: What can you do?

DEME: Not the right place.

ROMULUS: Why not? *(To Andi:)* What needs doin'?

DEME: This valley's dying.

ROMULUS: You got it flipped. They're bringing it back. *(To Andi:)* You got something for me, right?

ANDI: We got work for everybody that wants it.

ROMULUS: I want it.

DEME: There are no polar bears here.

ROMULUS: How do you know they're anywhere?

ANDI: The water in the valley is headed this way. We're gonna dam it up, use it for the gardens. You can help with that.

DEME: *(To Andi:)* Thanks, but we won't be staying.

ANDI: If we can just get the salt out.

ROMULUS: I'll help.

DEME: We'll do what we need for a couple weeks of road food.

ROMULUS: I don't care about stupid polar bears.

ANDI: Polar bears?

DEME: We're going north. That's where they are.

ANDI: Polar bears are killers.

DEME: We'll be safe there.

ANDI: You're safe here.

DEME: Are we?

ANDI: Things are good here.

ROMULUS: I want to stay.

ANDI: *(Beat.)* You don't look for a killer—unless you want to die.

SCENE 4

(Later that day. Cassie approaches Romulus, who writes in a small, ratty notebook. Andi and Deme are in their respective corners of the stage, unlit.)

CASSIE: Dinner's almost ready.

ROMULUS: Not from a can?

CASSIE: Not from a can. What's that?

ROMULUS: Helps me remember things.

CASSIE: What kind of things?

ROMULUS: Things I don't want to forget.

(There's an awkward silence.)

CASSIE: Sorry about my sister.	**ROMULUS:** Sorry about my sister.

(Another awkward silence.)

CASSIE: Not your fault.	**ROMULUS:** Not your fault.

(Again, awkward, but there's a shared recognition of the ridiculousness of the moment, and a hint of attraction in the air.)

CASSIE: What's it like?

ROMULUS: What?

CASSIE: Out there.

(Romulus shrugs.)

What's that mean?

ROMULUS: Sometimes stuff just *is*, you know?

CASSIE: *Is* good or *is* bad?

ROMULUS: How come there's no other guys?

CASSIE: Sometimes stuff just *is.* *(Beat.)* There were, where we used to be. The twins, Matthew and Luke. Then there was John...and Peter. Peter was the funny one. He'd find these dead flowers on the ground, and he'd try to water them with spit and give them to me. One time, his mouth is so dry, there's hardly any spit and what there is can't get into the air—only he doesn't know it. And so he smiles and gives me these dead dandelions and then he realizes he's got this glob all over his chin, and he's trying to get it with his tongue while he's still smiling and bowing and holding out the flowers. I'm like, "Peter, I think the dandelions could use a few more drops." And he says, "I think you're right." And he wipes them on his chin and put them in my hand. *(Beat.)* He was the first to go. Andi says that's so he could be at the gates for us. I don't know what that means. I just know he's gone.

ROMULUS: I think I would've liked him.

(Cassie nods.)

CASSIE: And then we left and found this place.

ROMULUS: Why do they say you see things?

CASSIE: Because I do.

ROMULUS: How?

(Cassie shrugs.)

CASSIE: *(Beat.)* I've got some pictures before the—Andi calls it Tipping Day.

ROMULUS: Pictures of what?

CASSIE: *(Continuing her thought:)* Like it was happening a little all the time. Just a little. So little you don't even notice. Until one day it just...tipped.

(She pantomimes a tipping motion with her hands.)

ROMULUS: I want to see the pictures.

CASSIE: It's almost like that here. Like it was before.

ROMULUS: Please.

CASSIE: I can show you.

ROMULUS: I'd like that.

(He reaches out and takes her hand. Enter Adam and Eve.)

EVE: The spa!

(Enter Scrubs from another direction.)

ADAM AND EVE: *(Rocking out:)* Spa spa spa [etc.]

EVE: They've got this glass that makes the rocks hot.

ADAM: From the sun.

EVE: And they steam.

ADAM: Best ever...

SCRUBS: What about the party pool?

ROMULUS: That was good times.

ADAM: That was nothing.

CASSIE: What's the party pool?

EVE: Zero.

ADAM: The spa is the new party pool.

ROMULUS: Just this place we used to go.

ADAM: The party pool is dead. Long live the party spa.

SCRUBS: The party spa.

ADAM, EVE AND SCRUBS: Party spa! Party spa! [etc.]

(It looks like they're about to parade off.)

ANDI: Dinner time.

ADAM, EVE AND SCRUBS: Party spa...

ADAM: After dinner! Party spa—

EVE, SCRUBS AND ROMULUS: After dinner!

(All start to dance offstage as the lights dim, herded by Andi.)

ROMULUS: You should come.

CASSIE: I've been to the spa before.

ROMULUS: But not the party spa!

(Romulus and Cassie hurry to catch up. Deme remains, almost reclusive in one corner, watching.)

SCENE 5

(After dinner. From offstage, we hear "party spa, party spa" and other improvised sounds of fun. On stage, Cassie and Andi are in one area, and Romulus and Deme are in another. The conversations are separate, though intertwined.)

ROMULUS: Come on—everybody's there.

DEME: The party spa?

ANDI: This is a bad idea.

CASSIE: Come on—it's just one night.

ROMULUS: *(Singing the jingle from before:)* Friday night is party night.

ANDI: Pretty soon it'll be just one more night and one more night after that—

DEME: How do you even know it's Friday?

ROMULUS: The magic watch that never stops.

CASSIE: You say you want it to be normal, but you don't want us to do normal things.

ANDI: The party spa is normal?

DEME: Things don't stay forever, Romey.

CASSIE: Romey says it'll be the most fun I ever had.

ANDI: Romey?

ROMULUS: You always see the worst in everything.

ANDI: *(Realizing Cassie likes him—teasing:)* Romey...well, if Romey says...

DEME: I see what's real.

ANDI: Romey Romey Romey...

CASSIE: *(Embarrassed:)* Stop.

ANDI: Romey –

CASSIE: Stop.

ANDI: *(Finishes "Romeo":)* – O.

ROMULUS: Your polar bears aren't real.

CASSIE: Did you just smile?

ANDI: No.

DEME: They are.

ROMULUS: They're ghosts. It's like some guy a long time ago said, "I think there's some polar bears up north." Or maybe he didn't even say up north. Maybe your head made that up. Maybe all he said was "I saw polar bears once. At the zoo. Before everything fell apart. Before it all tipped."

ANDI: You still see it green, right?

CASSIE: Green as grass grows.

ANDI: *(Beat.)* Go – with Romey.

CASSIE: Thanks!

(Cassie gives Andi a hug and starts to go, lingering at the edge of the stage as if waiting for Romulus.)

ROMULUS: You should come.

DEME: We need to go.

ROMULUS: Come on – it'll be like it used to be. Only better.

DEME: *(Beat.)* I'll look. For a minute.

(He meets up with Cassie.)

ROMULUS: To the party spa!

(He starts to leave with Cassie, then reaches back and tugs at Deme. She gives in and exits with them.)

SCENE 6

(Enter Scrubs, fresh from the party spa. She should have her own light, and Deme should stay unlit and almost invisible.)

SCRUBS: Deme ain't watchin', so I finally get to speak my mind. Whole time we're partyin' it up at the spa, she's watchin' us. I can't barely enjoy the wet hot 'cause I can feel her staring a hole through me, through everybody. *(Beat.)* And while we're on the subject, that part about me being half-dead, that's what we call an exaggeration. For real I'm just sleepin on the side of the road, catchin' my breath. Don't let her tell you different. My mom is sleepin' too. *(Beat.)* Only reason I even stick with her is that sometimes she teaches me stuff, only I hate all the stuff she teaches me. It's boring and useless. Like the word euphemism. Sleeping is a euphemism for dead.

(The lights come up across more of the stage, and Scrubs joins Romulus, Adam, Eve, Cassie and some of the New San Franciscans, all dressed as if they've just come from the party spa – perhaps similarly to their party pool attire of earlier. Deme observes from a distance, and Andi enters sometime during this choral moment. Each of these lines could be said by any of the New San Franciscans, or anyone but Deme, Cassie, Romulus or Andi.)

CHORUS OF NEW SAN FRANCISCANS: She needs to stop staring.
She needs to stop talking.
Maybe she's right.
The ground is turning browner.
The plants are dying.
You're imagining it.
She says it, and now you're seeing it.
Listen to Cassie, not to her.
(To Romulus:) Why did you bring her to the party spa?

She ruined everything.
The garden is fine.
Not if we waste the water.
You sound like her.
You sound like my mother.
I miss my mom.
I miss mine too.

(Suddenly – and it's possible there could be a lighting change – the chorus shifts into an expressionistic moment that they are reliving:)

CHORUS OF NEW SAN FRANCISCANS: Breaking news: units of the California National Guard have opened fire on Nevadans guarding the Colorado River aquifer.
The governor of California has denied all responsibility and said –
These units are acting alone.
Planes are coming.
Anonymous sources confirm California acted while it still had sufficient supplies of oil to carry out an attack.
Nevada retaliates.
Mass evacuations of flooded coastal regions are underway.
Fires are burning out of control and there is not enough water to put them out.
People are being left for dead.
On the side of the road.
Or worse.
There is panic.
Things are falling apart.
Breaking down.
It's chaos.

ANDI: Stop!

(All comes to a grinding halt. Silence. It's as if that choral

moment never was – almost.)

(Mostly directed at Deme:) There was a man. A week ago.

CASSIE: What man?

ANDI: A man in the valley. I didn't tell you. He was just passing through. No reason to tell you about a man just passing through. *(Beat.)* I gave him half my water. He says, "You give me the other half, I'll tell you a story you won't never believe, but that don't mean it's a lie." I pour him all but one mouthful, and he moves real close and whispers, "The polar bears. They're real, and I know where they are." No matter what I say, he won't say another word. "I've said too much," he says, and he takes a swallow, and then he's gone.

DEME: Where did he go?

(Andi points north.)

A week?

ANDI: Give or take.

CASSIE: Why didn't you say something?

ANDI: Maybe 10.

CASSIE: You should have said something.

ANDI: Like what? A man came and then he left. It's not like the world ended. People are out there.

CASSIE: Not around here.

DEME: *(To Romulus:)* We'll leave soon as it's light.

ADAM: Not me.

EVE: We like it here. At the spa.

ANDI: You work, you stay.

EVE: Adam and Eve, workers

Party weekends at the spa
Good, better and best.

ADAM: That's it, baby.

DEME: Nobody says you gotta come.

SCRUBS: I'm not goin' neither.

DEME: Either.

SCRUBS: *Either* way, I'm stayin' here.

ADAM: If we gotta work tomorrow, then tonight...I'm going back to the party spa!

SCRUBS: Rock on!

EVE: Woohoo!

(Adam, Eve and Scrubs take off running, along with most of the New San Franciscans. Beat.)

CASSIE: I'll go.

ANDI: *(Not expecting this:)* What?!

CASSIE: I said I'm going.

ANDI: No.

CASSIE: I wasn't asking.

ANDI: You're too young.

CASSIE: I'm almost 16.

ANDI: There's nothing out there.

CASSIE: There's a man.

ANDI: There's no—

CASSIE: How do you know if you never go? For three years, it's been us all alone, this tiny little miracle, but the water's creeping in the valley—

ANDI: We're damming it up.

CASSIE: But is that all there is? Is this all there's ever gonna be?

ANDI: How do you know it'll be any better out there?

DEME: There's hope out there.

ANDI: *(To Deme:)* This isn't your business.

DEME: *(To Cassie:)* One day real soon, we're going to get to a place that's going to make this all look like a lot of nothing.

ROMULUS: I don't know if I can do this again.

DEME: *(Beat.)* Romey?

ANDI: *(To Cassie:)* We're making it work here.

ROMULUS: I said I wanted to stay here.

DEME: But it's different now.

CASSIE: Making it work...

DEME: Now there's a man says the same thing.

ROMULUS: Is there?

DEME: *(Continuing her thought:)* They're real for sure.

ANDI: *(Responding to Cassie:)* That's right.

ROMULUS: This isn't a bad place.

DEME: I never said it was.

CASSIE: But for how long?

DEME: It's not where we need to be.

ANDI: Don't listen to her. It's New San Francisco—we can turn it into anything we want.

DEME: I'm leaving in the morning.

CASSIE: I'm coming with.

ANDI: You said so yourself. It'll be green.

DEME: They're not ghosts, Romey.

ROMULUS: First the party pool, now the party spa. Why you always want to leave the good stuff?

ANDI: There's work and food and plenty of water...you can stay here with Romey, and we can make it anything you want it to be.

CASSIE: The green I saw—it's not here.

(Deme walks out of the scene, as all else freezes—but this time, Romulus joins her.)

ROMULUS: My watch stopped.

DEME: Wasn't going to last forever.

ROMULUS: *(Beat.)* Say we find 'em—what then?

DEME: I don't know. But I think when we do, we'll know what to do. *(Beat—she steps into her own moment:)* The ground is white. The air is crisp, and it feels fresh on our skin and blowing through our hair, but not cold. And the water runs in a clear stream. We'll lie down to rest and the ground will be soft like fur. Like baby polar bears. And we'll sleep and wake up refreshed, ready to begin again.

(Deme rejoins Romulus.)

ROMULUS: I'm afraid without my watch.

(Cassie joins them, as the lights fade on all but the three of them.)

DEME: *(Pointing into the evening sky:)* See that star? We'll just keep walking toward it.

CASSIE: It looks like the tip of a bear's tail.

ROMULUS: What if we never get there?

DEME: We'll just keep walking.

(The lights fade to black. End of Act I.)

ACT II: URSA MAJOR

SCENE 1

(North of New San Francisco. A blighted landscape in the early evening. Deme enters ahead of Romulus and Cassie. All are dressed for the road, their heads well-covered to shield them from the sun. They stop and survey their surroundings. Cassie looks back at where they came.)

CASSIE: I can't see the lights.

ROMULUS: Maybe they didn't turn them on yet.

CASSIE: It's getting dark. They shoulda turned them on.

(Romulus taps his watch, trying to get it to work.)

Maybe something's wrong.

DEME: We're over a hill. Two hills. We can't see it from here. *(Beat.)* We'll rest now.

(Deme pulls out food from her pack.)

Don't eat too much.

CASSIE: Took all we could carry.

DEME: Don't know how long it's gotta last.

CASSIE: The fresh'll go bad if we don't eat it.

ROMULUS: I think I can fix this.

DEME: The battery's dead.

ROMULUS: I'm gonna fix it!

DEME: You can't.

CASSIE: *(Beat.)* Hey—guess what I brought.

DEME: What?

CASSIE: Romey, guess what I brought. *(Beat.)* Pictures.

ROMULUS: The pictures from before?!

(Cassie opens her pack and pulls out an envelope that is wrapped several times. She unwraps it carefully as Deme and Romulus gather around. She presents the first picture.)

CASSIE: That's Venice.

ROMULUS: Where's that?

DEME: It was part of Los Angeles...before.

ROMULUS: And now?

DEME: Gone. *(Beat.)* There used to be this place, Muscle Beach. It was famous. All these big, big guys right by the Boardwalk, arms bigger than your legs. *Both* your legs.

ROMULUS: No way.

CASSIE: I think I heard of that.

ROMULUS: I never heard of—

DEME: Shh!

ROMULUS: What?

(Deme holds up a hand for silence. Beat.)

DEME: *(Quietly:)* There's someone out there.

ROMULUS: I don't hear any—

DEME: Someone's there.

ROMULUS: Maybe it's just a dog.

DEME: When's the last time you saw a dog?

ROMULUS: Why do you never listen to anything I say?

DEME: Try being right once.

ROMULUS: I am too—

CASSIE: I feel it too.

ROMULUS: *(Beat.)* What do we do?

DEME: Act normal. Keep talking.

(Romulus starts to reach for his makeshift weapon.)

Don't.

ROMULUS: But—

DEME: *(Forced:)* Show us another one.

(Romulus stops himself, but his hand doesn't go too far from his weapon.)

ROMULUS: We can't just sit around and—

DEME: *(Sotto:)* What do you want us to do? *(Louder:)* Cassie, what other ones you got?

(Cassie pulls out a trio of picture postcards.)

CASSIE: The world's biggest ball of yarn.

DEME: What if there's 10 of them out there?

CASSIE: It's weird. There's three pictures. Always thought they were the same, just shot from different sides or something.

ROMULUS: We just gonna wait until they come?

CASSIE: But one says Nevada, one says Minnesota, and one says Illinois.

DEME: I'm not goin' out into the nowhere til I know what's what.

CASSIE: They can't all be the biggest.

ROMULUS: *(Beat.)* You ever just wish you could walk into the postcard?

CASSIE: You wanna walk into the world's biggest ball of yarn?

(Romulus steps into his own light and out of real time.)

ROMULUS: I wanna sit on the green grass and feel the wind, and there's no desert dust—it's just cool and clean and it blows through my hair. And the sun is warm, but it's not hot and burning. It's soft and it's...you can feel the grass on your toes. It's soft and spongy and every blade smells green and alive. And it's like this perfect moment: me, the world's biggest ball of yarn that's in Nevada or Minnesota or Illinois, but it doesn't matter and there's this feeling that you just can't explain, only you don't ever want to leave it. Like my mom's hand on my shoulder.

(Lights come back up.)

Did Mom have soft hands?

DEME: Romey, it's been so long.

ROMULUS: Did she?

DEME: I was six.

ROMULUS: *(Beat.)* Deme?

DEME: Her face flutters in and out of my head. Can't lock it in.

ROMULUS: Try to remember. Please.

DEME: *(Beat.)* She had...elegant hands.

ROMULUS: Elegant.

DEME: They were pale.

ROMULUS: Were they soft?

DEME: They were perfect.

ROMULUS: I knew it.

CASSIE: *(Beat.)* It's only one person.

DEME: How do you—

CASSIE: Because I do. *(To Deme:)* You know the one.

DEME: That one?

CASSIE: That one.

DEME: *(Beat.)* You comin' out, or you gonna keep snake slinking behind us?

(Beat. Scrubs comes out of the darkness.)

SCRUBS: What you lookin' at?

ROMULUS: Nothin'.

DEME: *(Beat. To Scrubs:)* You hungry?

SCRUBS: Maybe.

(Deme parcels out some food, but doesn't give it to Scrubs yet.)

CASSIE: Why are you here?

SCRUBS: What you got?

CASSIE: *(To Scrubs:)* My sister send you?

ROMULUS: What you doin' here?

SCRUBS: Sittin. What you doin'?

ROMULUS: Eatin'.

CASSIE: Is my sister OK?

SCRUBS: Right as...how's that go? Right as...

DEME: Rain.

SCRUBS: What's that?

DEME: You know what rain is.

SCRUBS: Ain't never seen it.

ROMULUS: I ever seen it?

DEME: When you were little.

CASSIE: Answer my question.

DEME: Rain's dried up and turned to spit.

SCRUBS: She's right as rain.

CASSIE: Romey, make her—

ROMULUS: Scrubs, quit the riddles.

SCRUBS: I'm hungry.

(Deme pulls the food away.)

DEME: Tell.

(Scrubs reaches out for the food. Deme again moves it away.)

ROMULUS: You heard her.

SCRUBS: *(To Romulus:)* I'm not scared of you.

CASSIE: You will be.

(Cassie moves toward her threateningly. Deme gets between them.)

ECHO: *(Off:)* You will be.

(The others stop their jostling.)

DEME: What was that?

ECHO: *(Off:)* What was that?

DEME: You hear it?

ECHO: *(Off:)* You hear it?

CASSIE: It's an echo.

ECHO: *(Off:)* It's an echo.

ROMULUS: Echo don't sound like somebody else.

ECHO: *(Off:)* Echo don't sound like somebody else.

(They pull together so that they can't be overheard.)

ROMULUS: Is it one?

SCRUBS: I hear one.

DEME: Don't mean it's the only one.

ROMULUS: *(To Deme:)* You shouldn'ta picked here.

DEME: You were tired.

ROMULUS: Wasn't.

SCRUBS: *(Mocking Romulus:)* Oh, Deme, make me a bed and tuck me, I'm so tired.

ROMULUS: Shut it, Scrubs.

ECHO: *(Off:)* Shut it, Scrubs.

DEME: *(To Scrubs:)* One more word I will throw you back into the nowhere.

SCRUBS: Nah you wouldn't.

DEME: Try.

SCRUBS: Try. **ECHO:** *(Off:)* Try.

DEME: Don't you start.

ECHO: *(Off:)* Don't you start.

DEME: *(Beat.)* Hello?

ECHO: *(Off:)* Hello?

DEME: Who's there?

ECHO: *(Off:)* Who's there?

DEME: What's your name?

ECHO: *(Off:)* What's your name?

(Cassie and Romulus grab their weapons and start to sneak off, but Deme holds up a hand and they stop.)

DEME: Are you hungry?

ECHO: *(Off:)* Are you hungry?

ROMULUS: We don't have enough—

DEME: We'll feed him Scrubs if she doesn't shut it. *(Putting food on the ground nearby:)* I'm putting it right here.

(There's a long silence.)

It's right here. Just come and get it.

(Another long silence.)

CASSIE: He stopped.

SCRUBS: I ain't sleepin' with a creeper out in the nowhere.

ROMULUS: A creeper like you?

SCRUBS: Was not.

ROMULUS: Sneakin' like half a shadow.

SCRUBS: You knew it was me. Can't be creepin' if you knew it was me.

ROMULUS: *(Beat.)* Now what?

DEME: Wait.

CASSIE: Let us go out into the—

DEME: Light's fadin'.

CASSIE: We got time.

DEME: Not for a nowhere we don't know.

(Long silence.)

ROMULUS: I'm not as happy as I was.

DEME: *(Beat.)* 'Cause you're older.

ROMULUS: Older is sad?

DEME: Older knows more. Weighs your brain.

SCRUBS: Like rocks.

ROMULUS: I'm starting to forget the party pool. I know it was there. I know we went swimming.

SCRUBS: We went dancing—

ROMULUS: But I can't see it. *(Beat. Half-singing:)* Friday night is party night. *(Not singing:)* I sang that.

SCRUBS: Bad as bricks.

ROMULUS: *(Singing again:)* Friday night is party night. Make the work week come out right. *(Not singing:)* And then we'd get the party water and swim in the party pool—

SCRUBS: And then we left and Tina and Ike went goners and we went to the party spa and Adam and Eve stayed and she came with and I came back and now we're here. The end.

(Enter ECHO. He is no more than Scrubs' age, preferably younger if your production has access to a younger acting pool. He speaks with a stutter, except when he echoes another character.)

ECHO: I-i-is th-th-that a-a-a stuh-stuh-stuh-uh-r-ry?

SCRUBS: A what?

ECHO: A what?

DEME: A story?

(Echo nods. Beat as he calculates the path to the food and whether he can make it there safely. He goes for the food and eats like he hasn't eaten in forever.)

SCRUBS: We gonna watch him eat?

DEME: He needs it more than you.

SCRUBS: How you know?

DEME: When I found you—

SCRUBS: *(Imitating Deme:)* You was a stick-thin carcass on the side of the road, a few hours short of a prophet to send you home. *(As herself:)* Heard you 'til the rain comes.

(Cassie glides toward Echo.)

CASSIE: It's good, isn't it?

(Echo continues to eat, but gets jumpy as Cassie draws closer.)

I'm not gonna hurt you.

ECHO: I'm not gonna hurt you.

CASSIE: *(Indicates herself:)* Cassie.

(Silence.)

Do you have a name?

ECHO: Do you have a name?

CASSIE: *(Beat.)* What if we call you...Echo? *(Points at him:)* Echo.

ECHO: Echo.

CASSIE: Do you live near here?

(Silence. Scrubs starts to yank at his dish. He tries to hold onto it.)

It's OK.

ECHO: They d-d-don't l-l-et me b-b-be i-i-n-n the stuh-stuh-ry.

CASSIE: Who's they?

DEME: Who doesn't let you? *(Slapping at Scrubs' hand:)* Scrubs!

ROMULUS: What story?

(Scrubs succeeds in grabbing the dish. Echo covers his ears and rocks.)

CASSIE: Hey. Hey.

DEME: Scrubs, I mean it!

SCRUBS: You said not another word.

(Romulus chases after Scrubs.)

CASSIE: Look at this. *(Showing Echo the postcards:)* World's biggest ball of yarn.

ECHO: World's biggest ball of yarn.

(Romulus chases Scrubs back toward Deme, who grabs the dish back. Scrubs makes herself scarce, getting as far away as possible as Deme puts the food back in front of Echo, who eats.)

W-w-what's ya-ya yarn?

CASSIE: Yarn is—it's... *(To Romulus:)* What's yarn exactly?

(Romulus thinks, then shrugs.)

DEME: It's like string.

(That doesn't help Echo.)

String?

ECHO: String?

(Deme searches in her pack and finds some string.)

DEME: *(Holding it up:)* String.

ECHO: *(Examining it:)* String.

DEME: Where do you live?

ECHO: S-st-string.

(He runs off with what's left of "his" food.)

DEME: Hey!

(Cassie and Deme exit after him. Beat. Enter Cassie and Deme.)

He's gone.

SCRUBS: 'Course he is. You're slower than quicksand.

DEME: You don't even know what quicksand is.

SCRUBS: I know what it ain't.

DEME: What's that?

SCRUBS: Fast.

CASSIE: It's dark.

SCRUBS: So?

CASSIE: It's *his* dark.

SCRUBS: I can find him.

ROMULUS: If they couldn't catch him—

SCRUBS: He's got feet, don't he?

CASSIE: How's he gonna get away without feet?

SCRUBS: Feet leave tracks, and I'm tops at trackin' tracks. *(Beat.)* I tracked you, didn't I?

ROMULUS: You knew we were goin' this way.

SCRUBS: If I leave now—

DEME: You won't find him in the dark. We don't live in miracle days.

SCRUBS: We're alive. Ain't that miracle enough?

DEME: Wait 'til light.

SCRUBS: How we gonna sleep with him out there?

CASSIE: He's not scary.

DEME: One watches, the rest sleep.

SCRUBS: Yeah, but—

DEME: He was out there before.

CASSIE: Truth.

ROMULUS: Always someone out there in the somewhere.

SCRUBS: But—

DEME: But nothing.

ROMULUS: Nothing to be done.

DEME: *(Something sparks:)* Dad said that. *(Beat.)* You remember that?

ROMULUS: I said it.

DEME: I never told you that.

ROMULUS: Then I must remember.

DEME: Nothing to be done. *(Beat.)* Mom and Dad went to this play. Do you remember Amanda, who used to watch us? I was watching TV on the couch with Amanda until I fell asleep, and then Mom and Dad are home and Dad is saying "Nothing to be done" and chasing me around the living room.

Run run run nothing to be done! And he catches me and he tickles me and I scream from the tickling and he lets me go and starts all over. Mom is yelling don't wake Romey and Dad just keeps saying nothing to be done and finally we all fall and laugh on the floor. *(Beat.)* It was the one time Dad did something funny. *(Beat.)* One watches, three sleep.

ROMULUS: I'm not tired.

DEME: Wake me before you are.

(Cassie, Deme and Scrubs pick their spots and settle down to sleep. Romulus keeps watch. Beat. Once he's sure they're asleep, he pulls out a ratty book – not his writing notebook.)

ROMULUS: I found this book. We're going through a squat like we do when we find one that's got nobody in it, which is always. Water food weapons power coin clothes fun and games, always in that order. Stick to the order – it might save your life. And this squat – no, this *house* – is so beautiful I want to live in it forever. They got windows like you wouldn't believe, and a pool that makes the party pool look like a bucket. No, like a puddle. Only the water's gone of course. And they got a giant bed and an almost giant bed and then just a really big bed – they got so many beds you could sleep in a different bed every day for a week. And if I could just get one night in even the really big bed, but Deme says the big dead is right behind and gotta keep moving. So I'm grabbin' everything I can, everything I can fit in every pocket, and I open a door and it's a library. A library. With books. Fancy books with fancy covers and gold and silver writing. *(Beat.)* Water food weapons power coin clothes fun and games. Don't jump the order. No way does a book beat a can of tuna. No way does a book beat a can of anything. I can hear Deme screamin' at me in my head. And I look at all the gold and silver books and I know they're too big and let me just leave now before I— It's so thin and the corner of the cover is folded over, but the cover has these two tiny people and this tree that looks dead and a whole lotta empty, and I just gotta have it, cause it looks like us. *(Beat.)* I read it when Deme's gone. I've read it 17 times. Except for the end. Somebody ripped out the last three pages. So I don't know if the man comes or not. *(From the play:)* Nothing to be done. *(Beat.)* I was two when Dad came home from the play, but I still remember. And when I do the play, I feel him watching. I know it's not his face I see, but it's my make-believe dad's face, and he's smiling.

(Romulus continues to keep watch as the lights dim.)

SCENE 2

(The next morning. Deme shakes Romulus awake. There is no sign of Scrubs or Cassie.)

ROMULUS: I was having the best dream.

DEME: Daylight's burnin.

ROMULUS: Let it burn.

DEME: Gonna burn you with it. *(Beat.)* It's dustin' those tracks by the second.

ROMULUS: Tracks to the nowhere.

DEME: Gotta be goin' somewhere. Too small to be alone.

ROMULUS: Lotta stuff shouldn't be but is. *(Beat.)* Just five more minutes.

DEME: How you gonna know five minutes?

ROMULUS: I'll count sheep.

DEME: How you gonna count sheep if you're asleep?

ROMULUS: It's a secret.

DEME: You don't even know what a sheep is.

ROMULUS: I read about 'em in one of those big empty houses. *(Brief pause.)* They looked so soft. This doesn't count in my sheep time.

DEME: There's no time to—

ROMULUS: Shhh... I'm sheeping.

(Beat. The lights come up elsewhere on stage. Scrubs, nearby but not close enough to be visible, looks at tracks when Cassie comes up on her.)

CASSIE: Deme said don't wander.

SCRUBS: Nobody's the boss of me but me.

CASSIE: And while you're bossin', they're gonna ambush your pretty little face.

SCRUBS: My face is not pretty.

CASSIE: Yeah you got that right.

SCRUBS: Shut up. Ain't no ambush gonna ambush me.

CASSIE: Better check your memory.

SCRUBS: You're the one gonna bring 'em down on us. *(Beat.)* Why don't you go back to Romey. *(Mocking:)* Oh, Romey. Romey.

CASSIE: Least I got somebody.

SCRUBS: You got him?

CASSIE: Yeah. And he's got me.

SCRUBS: And Deme *(Snaps her fingers:)* and he'll be gone.

CASSIE: Maybe we'll all be gone and you'll be all alone in the nowhere.

SCRUBS: Suits me. *(Beat. Pointing at tracks:)* This is him.

CASSIE: You sure?

SCRUBS: Sure as sure it ain't gonna rain today.

(Pause.)

CASSIE: So now what?

SCRUBS: Well, you think she's gonna be more mad I ran off or more glad I found what needs finding?

CASSIE: If I had a coin, I'd flip it.

SCRUBS: Then you better tell her. Tell her and Romey. *(Indicating the tracks:)* I'll keep 'em fresh.

(Scrubs makes as if to take cover, while Cassie walks back to camp. She stops.)

CASSIE: I like Romey. How messed up is that? *(Beat.)* Maybe it's 'cause he's here and nobody else is. Maybe if I had more choices he wouldn't even be in my top 10. Maybe he wouldn't even be on the list. But he's the only boy I've seen in a long time, and I don't know yet if he's a great one, but I'm pretty sure he's at least a good one. *(Beat.)* I found this old video of my mom and dad, from before. My mom, she's all smiling and giggling and she says my dad's "the one" for her. The one. Maybe that's all there needs to be: one. And in 50 years, I'll be in my video, telling our kids that Romey was the one. The only man I ever loved. Love. The whole idea of loving someone right now seems like the most absurd thing in the world. Maybe that's why we have to do it.

(The lights dim, then come up full, as Deme, Scrubs, Romey and Cassie are at the tracks.)

They go off that way.

ROMULUS: Maybe they do, but...

(Beat as they realize that they're standing on the edge of a deserted campsite.)

SCRUBS: Trackpot.

(Scrubs starts to move toward the camp.)

DEME: Wait.

ROMULUS: Empty now.

DEME: Empty and gone don't always travel together.

SCRUBS: Can't stand here 'til we're dead!

DEME: I don't like this.

ROMULUS: Empty is empty. *(Starting to go toward the camp:)* Maybe they left some cans.

DEME: Romey, stay.

ROMULUS: I'm not a dog.

SCRUBS: Ruff. Ruff. Here, boy!

(Romulus chases after Scrubs.)

Runs like a dog to me!

(He barks at her. She barks back.)

DEME: Stop.

(They keep up the barking and chasing. It's degenerated into a game.)

We don't know what's out there.

CASSIE: Deme's right.

(Romulus stops by Cassie and nuzzles against her like a dog.)

Stop it.

(He doesn't stop.)

Stop.

(He wins her over. Beat. She pets him.)

ROMULUS: *(Playful:)* Ruff.

(There's the SOUND OF BARKING DOGS. Beat.)

What's that?

CASSIE: Scrubs, stop it!

SCRUBS: I ain't 10 dogs at once!

DEME: It's all 'round.

NOAH: *(Off:)* Don't move.

DEME: Who are you?

NOAH: *(Off:)* Our dogs are hungry. We'll ask the questions.

(Deme and the others form a defensive circle. The "dogs" bark in such a way as to pan around them.)

Why did you come here?

CASSIE: Those aren't dogs.

DEME: Followed some tracks.

SCRUBS: When you ever heard a dog?

DEME: We thought there might be people.

CASSIE: We had one for a while. Back when there were boys.

SCRUBS: What happened to it?

NOAH: *(Off:)* If you have weapons, toss them out.

CASSIE: What do you think?

DEME: Dogs or no, there's a whole lotta something out there. *(To Noah:)* We're not lookin' for trouble.

NOAH: *(Off:)* Then drop your weapons.

DEME: *(Beat.)* We got cans.

SCRUBS: Those are ours!

ROMULUS: *(To Scrubs:)* How many of them *you* find?

NOAH: *(Off:)* What makes you think we can't just take them?

DEME: *(Pulls a knife and holds it to a can like it's a hostage:)* I think we can turn 'em in to trash on the ground before you get three steps.

(Romulus, Cassie and Scrubs all pull their knives.)

SCRUBS: *(Sotto to Deme:)* Can't we just eat 'em real fast?

(Beat.)

DEME: I'm putting a can out.

(The barking continues.)

NOAH: *(Off:)* Put your weapons down. Now.

DEME: It's peas.

(She opens the can and places it in front of her, then slowly puts her knife away. She gestures for Romulus, Cassie and Scrubs to put theirs away. Beat. They do, not necessarily happily. Beat. Enter a TEEN, one of the "Dogs." The Teen, eyeing Deme and the others, moves toward the can. Two steps forward, one step back, one to the side, constantly keeping an eye on Deme. The Teen gets to the can, still cautious, but then it all breaks down: enter the other DOGS, three or four to a dozen or more in number, just older than Romulus and looking like something out of Lord of the Flies, *their clothing in tatters, not enough skill to keep it mended. They race madly for the can. It's chaos fueled by raw hunger. One of them, MERCURY, limps and lags behind the others. Before Mercury can even get close, the peas are gone. Even Scrubs looks a little taken aback. Beat. As one of the Dogs taps on the can of peas, looking for any last scraps, enter NOAH. He's 19 – a year older than Deme. He has an air of authority, and his clothes were once very nice. Beat. Deme goes into her bag for a can of corn.)*

SCRUBS: C'mon – not the corn!

(Deme walks slowly toward Noah, as Romulus keeps an eye on the Dogs, his weapon almost out in case of trouble. Deme holds out the can of corn.)

What's he done for you?

ROMULUS: *(To Scrubs:)* What you ever done for anyone?

SCRUBS: Shut it.

(Noah takes the can of corn with a nod and examines it. Beat. He produces a spoon from his back pocket, then a ratty napkin. All of the Dogs' eyes are on him as he tucks the napkin into his shirt. He takes a spoonful and chews slowly, while his entire crew watches him and stares at the can with lust. Beat. He dabs at his mouth with his napkin, then folds it carefully and puts it and the spoon away. Beat. He puts the can on the ground. The Dogs start for it, but Noah's hand goes up. They stop. He looks at Mercury, who slowly and painfully heads toward the can. Mercury has one bite, two bites, then backs away. Noah nods, and the Dogs move in and obliterate the contents of the can.)

NOAH: If you wanted to poison us, you'd have done it on the first can.

(With the corn gone, the Dogs look to Deme.)

SCRUBS: Don't you dare.

ROMULUS: Shut it, Scrubs. *(Sotto to Deme:)* C'mon, Deme—didn't you give 'em enough?

DEME: *(To Noah:)* When's the last time you ate?

NOAH: Wednesday.

SCRUBS: When was that?

NOAH: Thirty-eight hours ago.

ROMULUS: How you know 38?

NOAH: I looked at my watch.

(Beat. Romulus is interested.)

ROMULUS: You have a—

(Noah indicates that the sun is his "watch.")

NOAH: If you're planning to rob us you'll die...of disappointment.

(Beat. Noah starts to laugh. The Dogs pick up his laughter. It's unnerving.)

SCRUBS: Stop that!

CASSIE: Deme?

ROMULUS: If it makes Scrubs crazy, I'm in.

(Romulus starts laughing. The Dogs abruptly stop laughing.)

What?

NOAH: We thought you might be someone else.

DEME: We're headed north.

DOGS: *(Part echo, part whisper:)* North...north...north...

SCRUBS: Stop that.

NOAH: With everything you can carry.

ROMULUS: *(At Scrubs:)* North...north...north...

DEME: Something like that.

SCRUBS: You'll be sorry.

NOAH: You've come to the right place.

DEME: Why's that?

NOAH: You've come from the south. You're walking in the right direction.

ROMULUS: North, north, north...

(Scrubs runs off.)

DEME: She'll be back.

ROMULUS: Like a roach.

CASSIE: You should be nicer to her.

ROMULUS: Why?

CASSIE: Because...

ROMULUS: Why?

CASSIE: What's she done?

ROMULUS: Why?

CASSIE: Stop.

ROMULUS: Why?

(She hits him. He covers himself.)

Wait. *(To Noah:)* You said you ate Wednesday.

NOAH: And...?

ROMULUS: And that was 38 hours ago.

NOAH: And...?

ROMULUS: That means it's Friday. *(Singing to Deme:)* Friday night is party night. Make the work week come out right!

DEME: There's no party pool here. *(To Noah:)* You said you thought we might be someone else.

ROMULUS: They gotta have something, right?

DEME: Who?

NOAH: Rumors.

DEME: Rumors of what?

ROMULUS: Fun? Party?

NOAH: Whispers on the wind.

ROMULUS: Anyone?

DEME: Whispering what?

ROMULUS: *(In slo-mo:)* Parr-tyyy.

NOAH: That they came up from the far south or maybe the east and they burn anything in the way—and what they don't burn wishes it did.

ROMULUS: C'mon.

DEME: That the is or the maybe?

NOAH: The maybe may not be far away.

(Beat. Echo appears on the ridge. The others look restive. Noah gestures to a couple of the Dogs, who chase Echo off.)

You've seen him before.

DEME: On the road.

NOAH: He's a thief.

(Lights up on Scrubs, elsewhere on stage, away from the others—just over the ridge somewhere. Enter Echo.)

SCRUBS: Not you.

ECHO: Not you.

SCRUBS: Stop that.

ECHO: Stop that.

SCRUBS: I'll hurt you.

ECHO: I'll—

(Scrubs makes as if to strike Echo, who dodges out of the way. Scrubs chases after him. He's like the fly she can't swat. Their chase takes them offstage. Back in the main camp, Cassie and Romulus have wandered off together.)

CASSIE: I don't like this place.

ROMULUS: You'd like it more if we had some fun.

CASSIE: Look at them.

ROMULUS: Can I look at you?

CASSIE: Stop.

ROMULUS: Why?

CASSIE: Don't start.

ROMULUS: No. For real. Why?

CASSIE: Your sister, all of them...

ROMULUS: So if it was just you and me...

CASSIE: *(Beat.)* Sure.

ROMULUS: *(Checking around:)* Deme's talk talk talking, they're off in spaceland, and I'm gonna look at you.

(He stares at her. Beat.)

CASSIE: Romey.

ROMULUS: Do you want me to stop?

CASSIE: No.

(They continue to sit and look at each other. Deme talks to Noah:)

DEME: If there's no food here...you can't stay where there's no food.

NOAH: There used to be the most beautiful apple trees. Gala apples, they call them. For two whole months it rained apples. And the deer loved apples—I can cook venison with apples in 17 different ways. But the trees died and the deer left and we've ripped apart everything within three days' walk. *(Beat.)* Amazing the trees survived as long as they did.

DEME: You have to leave.

NOAH: And go where?

DEME: *(Beat.)* Come north—with us.

NOAH: We're not like you. When I found them, they were huddling in what was left of their classroom, still in their uniforms. They'd been living off the vending machines, but they were out of change and somehow even after the Nevada National Guard 41st Air Wing destroyed everything we'd ever known in the space of 23 minutes, it didn't occur to them that nobody'd care if they stole some stale pretzels.

DEME: That was a long time ago.

NOAH: Was it? *(Beat.)* It's like every one of them is Peter Pan pinned to that moment.

DEME: I know that story. *(Beat.)* Is there water?

NOAH: Not much.

DEME: Then how can you stay? *(Beat.)* It's not like you weren't somewhere else before you came here, right? You just do what you always do. What we always do. We move on.

NOAH: It's not that easy.

DEME: Left foot, right foot. *(Beat.)* Come north.

NOAH: We wouldn't make it.

DEME: No choice.

NOAH: *(To all:)* Did I hear someone mention fun? We can have fun here, can't we?

DEME: You have to do it.

NOAH: *(Beat. To the Dogs:)* Time for the pageant!

(The Dogs are suddenly a whir of activity, going into their tents and pulling out masks and costumes. Depending on cast size, the number of animals could vary: deer, rabbits, mountain lions, snakes, bears.)

DEME: You can't keep going while it all turns to nothing.

NOAH: I can't do much, as you can see. But that's one thing I'm good at. I've had the very best practice of all. *(Beat.)* I was playing piano. I used to take lessons three times a week from a woman with the whitest hair you've ever seen and a hand that would shake just a tiny bit, but in another life she'd played Carnegie Hall and been a soloist with every orchestra between Portland and Paris, and when she touched the piano the shake would vanish. I loved my lessons, and unlike almost any other seven-year-old on the planet, I loved to practice. I'd make my parents sit in the easy chairs by the window and play "concerts" for them. *(Beat.)* One time my mother got up in the middle of a movement of Tchaikovsky. I stopped and started banging on the keys like a maniac until she sat back down. And thus I trained my parents to stay until I played the very last note, and got up from my little booster bench. *(Beat.)* And on a beautiful April day, they are sitting there as I regale them with Mozart's Piano Concerto Number 15 in B-flat major, which would be extremely challenging at any age. They're still sitting there as we hear this far away thunder, and I look up from my Mozart and see the hint of a plume of distant dust through the window, but I don't stop playing, so they don't stop sitting, and they are still in their chairs when the entire side of the room by the windows falls away into nothing. I don't know what to do. A seven-year-old brain cannot process houses and parents winking into never agains, so I finish the 15th, but I am troubled by the middle C, which has gone terribly flat. *(Beat.)* I cry for half an hour—32 minutes, actually—but when it becomes clear that my piano is irrevocably broken, and that neither my parents nor the woman with the white hair will be coming back to listen to me play or for any other reason, I stop crying, close the cover, and two days later, I find *(Indicating the others:)* them. And we keep going. *(Beat.)* They're ready. *(Turning master of ceremonies:)* Mrs. Middleton's Former Pre-Kindergarten Drama Class Presents the Pageant of the Animals.

(The Dogs turned Animals form a procession, each stepping up awkwardly to deliver their line. It's as if they are frozen in time in pre-kindergarten. As they step up, they act out the motions and make sound effects.)

ANIMALS: The rabbit hops.
And the squirrel scampers.
The deer runs.
Chased by the mountain lion, which sprints and snarls.
And on the ground, the snake slithers.
The crow caws,
And the big brown bear lumbers, big and slow.
(Beat.)
March of the animals.
Parade of the animals.
Exodus of the animals.

ANIMAL 1: Away from the hot hot hot...

THE OTHER ANIMALS: *(Like an echo:)* To the north.

ANIMAL 2: Away from the dead and the brown.

THE OTHER ANIMALS: *(Echoing:)* To the north.

ANIMAL 3: Away from the fire in the sky.

VARIOUS ANIMALS: To a place where they could rest on living land.
North...north...north...
Drink the clear and clean.
North...north...north...

(The distant sky turns red. The pageant halts.)

ANIMAL 1: Fire in the sky!

NOAH: They've come.

CASSIE: It's New San Francisco.

ROMULUS: No, it's—

CASSIE: Those are the flares. Those are the flares they fire for the gatherers.

ROMULUS: It's just a red sky.

CASSIE: Warning flares.

DEME: We have to go.

NOAH: We can't outrun them.

DEME: That's three days away. We move smart, three days is like months in all this nowhere. Tonight we plan, tomorrow first light we go.

NOAH: You have to go now.

DEME: First light.

NOAH: The whisper on the wind is that they are not on foot.

(Beat. Echo appears on the ridge. He is dressed in a polar bear costume.)

DEME: *(To everyone:)* Take what you can carry.

SCRUBS: Gotta make us disappear into the nothing or it won't do no good.

DEME: Then make us disappear.

(The Animals spot Echo on the ridge. They look to Noah.)

NOAH: Leave him. It's all going to burn anyway.

(The Animals await further instructions from Noah, who seems unable to give them.)

DEME: All of you. You have five minutes. *(Beat.)* Now!

(The Animals spring into action, packing their things. Scrubs might grab some of them during the ensuing scene and get them to help her in obliterating their tracks. Echo too could help after he speaks.)

CASSIE: We have to go back.

DEME: We can't go back.

CASSIE: My sister –

DEME: She can take care of herself.

MERCURY: *(To Noah:)* I'm not fast anymore.

CASSIE: *(To Romulus:)* Tell her we have to –

NOAH: I know.

MERCURY: It's bad.

CASSIE: Whether she comes or not.

(Cassie goes to grab her pack.)

NOAH: I know.

ROMULUS: We can't just leave them.

DEME: Do you think there's a choice?

ROMULUS: If it was you, wouldn't you want me to come back?

DEME: I'd want you to be safe.

ROMULUS: You see anywhere safe?

DEME: There's safe and there's suicide.

ROMULUS: And what about Adam and Eve?

DEME: They made a choice.

ROMULUS: What if it was me?

DEME: It's not.

ECHO: And the bears turned white.

ROMULUS: Would you leave me too?

ECHO: As they marched into the north, the north of the blue sky and the crisp, clean water, the bears turned white.

CASSIE: We have to go back.

ECHO: The white bears live forever in the land of 60 degrees north, 135 degrees west, and the Aurora Borealis dances with joy above their heads.

NOAH: *(To Mercury:)* I've always wanted to see the ocean again. Want to come with?

DEME: *(To Noah, indicating Echo:)* What is he talking about?

NOAH: He finished the story.

DEME: Is it true?

NOAH: It's a story.

DEME: Where did it come from?

(Beat. Noah produces a makeshift "book." It's an illustrated series of pictures bound precariously together.)

NOAH: We found it in some house or a shack or by the side of the road—I don't remember. It was years ago, and it's become this story we always tell.

ROMULUS: It's just a book. Not even a book.

DEME: Not a book. A map.

CASSIE: *(Returning with her pack:)* Romey, it's time.

ROMULUS: It's just a story.

DEME: We have to believe.

CASSIE: My sister is real. *(Beat.)* I'm real.

SCRUBS: *(Returning:)* I got it all rigged.

CASSIE: Romey, we have to go.

SCRUBS: Ain't nobody gonna know we were ever.

DEME: Nothing to be done, Romulus.

(Romulus picks up his pack. Beat.)

ROMULUS: Deme, please.

DEME: We can hide in the mountains if we can get there before it's day.

NOAH: Mercury and I, we'll think of you fondly as we take in the ocean view.

DEME: *(Beat.)* I hear it's beautiful still.

NOAH: If only we could drink it. *(Beat.)* Mrs. Middleton's Former Pre-K Drama Class, the show must go on, and it's for you to make sure that it does.

ANIMALS: No, no, no, no...

NOAH: There comes a time when the director's job is done.

ANIMALS: No, no, no...

NOAH: You are going on a wonderful new tour. *(Beat.)* At long last, you are going to play the north.

CASSIE: We have to go now. You and me. *(Beat.)* I see us. I see us together on the road back to New San Francisco and we get there in time.

ROMULUS: *(Beat.)* I can't.

CASSIE: *(Beat.)* Coward.

ROMULUS: I am not afraid.

CASSIE: Yes. You are. Of her.

(Echo, still dressed as the polar bear, grabs a pack and goes up to Cassie.)

ECHO: I am not afraid.

NOAH: *(To the Animals:)* Go with the stage manager. She will keep you safe. *(To Mercury:)* The ocean plays a very special kind of music.

MERCURY: Is it far?

NOAH: Just over that hill, and the one after that.

(Noah and Mercury exit at Mercury's snail's pace.)

ROMULUS: Cassie.

CASSIE: Goodbye, Romulus. *(To Echo:)* Let's go.

(She exits with Echo.)

ROMULUS: Cassie!

ANIMALS: Cassie, Cassie, Cassie...

ROMULUS: You and your stupid, stupid polar bears.

DEME: I don't care if you hate me.

ROMULUS: Good. Because maybe I do.

DEME: Gotta be alive to hate.

SCRUBS: *(Beat.)* So...we goin'?

ROMULUS: You think I won't leave you.

DEME: We're goin'.

ROMULUS: You're wrong.

DEME: We go north.

(Everyone left on stage exits with Deme except Romulus. Beat. He follows them. The lights begin a slow fade. There's the distant sound of MOTORCYCLES, getting gradually closer. End of Act II.)

(If your production plans to have an intermission, it should be here.)

ACT III: NORTHERN LIGHTS

SCENE 1

(A month after the end of Ursa Major. PAN, fka Melinda, late teens, female and with something of a postmodern Hell's Angels look, stands alone in a spotlight.)

PAN: The thing about rules is they're made for the people making them. Do this. Don't do that. Do what we say. Do it now. Do it now, Melinda, or we'll beat your scrawny ass until it don't work no more. But then something happens, something that makes the rules go away. The rules that say wear your clothes right side out and go to school, that say don't take this sign, 'cause it's the only one left standing in 200 miles *(Brandishing what's left of a 65 mph speed limit sign:)* and you just gotta have it, are gone. And you're free. Air and sunshine free. Do anything you want free. Do everything you want free. *(Beat.)* But then all that chaos and take take taking gets old. And it hits you like a backhand: you need rules. You been missing 'em and you didn't even realize it. Only this time, you're the one that gets to make them. I'm the one that gets to make them. I'm the Pan, and this is the new Neverland.

(Pan disappears into the darkness, and lights up on Deme, Scrubs and Romulus, all dirtier than before, chained up in a windowless room. They are doing their best to sleep. Romulus stirs.)

DEME: *(To Romulus:)* You awake? *(Beat.)* You gotta talk to me sometime. *(Pause.)* Scrubs, you awake?

SCRUBS: I'm dreamin' about water.

ROMULUS: How's that goin'?

SCRUBS: Great—'til I wake up. *(Beat.)* Foot's asleep.

ROMULUS: My whole body's asleep.

SCRUBS: Hope they come soon.

DEME: Do you?

ROMULUS: How long you think we been down here?

DEME: Been tryin' to count the count.

ROMULUS: I asked Scrubs.

SCRUBS: This is bad as bad can be, but you two gotta bury it. Wish I was deaf.

ROMULUS: *(Beat. To Deme:)* How long you reckon?

DEME: Thirty if I didn't lose it.

ROMULUS: *(Not forgiving:)* Don't think we're good.

DEME: Fine.

ROMULUS: *(Beat.)* Las Vegas.

SCRUBS: What's that?

DEME: A place. *(Beat.)* How you know about Las Vegas?

ROMULUS: Ike was from Vegas.

SCRUBS: Vegas.

DEME: He was?

SCRUBS: I like that.

ROMULUS: Yeah.

SCRUBS: Ike from Vegas. Ike from Vegas that made it past the boom-boom-boom and then zzzap, a bug takes you out.

ROMULUS: He said they lived in the MGM Grand for a month.

SCRUBS: MGM?

ROMULUS: Hotel. He said inside they had no windows.

SCRUBS: No day, no night.

ROMULUS: His dad lost everything right before it was all goners.

DEME: How'd he even remember that?

ROMULUS: How do any of us remember anything? But we do. *(Beat. An out of time moment:)* Funny story. Not ha funny, but weird horrible unlucky lucky funny. Ike's dad, he loses all the money, the house, all three cars, all the all. So he goes into Ike's room, 'cause Ike's computer has a cam, and he records his goodbye, world see ya later and then he takes his .357 Magnum and splatters all over Ike's pillow. Hell's bells gonna ring before Ike sleeps in his dad's blood, so he's safe in the basement when wave one hits.

(Romulus rejoins the scene. Enter Pan with KALI, her lieutenant, and a couple of FOOT SOLDIERS.)

PAN: Good morning.

(There's no reply from Deme or the others.)

I said good morning.

SCRUBS: Ain't no sun.

PAN: Don't mean it's not morning.

DEME: Where are the others?

PAN: Here we go again. *(Beat.)* Don't you have any other questions?

DEME: When will you let us go?

PAN: Any *other* questions. *(Beat.)* Tell you what—if you ask me a new question, I might just answer it.

SCRUBS: Got anything good to eat?

PAN: Yes.

SCRUBS: *(Beat.)* And...?

PAN: What?

SCRUBS: Can we have it?

PAN: I love this asking and answering. Let's do it again soon.

SCRUBS: *(Beat.)* That's it?

PAN: This is the bold one, but not the smart one. *(Beat.)* Who's the smart one? *(To Romulus:)* Is that you? *(Pawing him with her stick:)* We have apples and oranges—fresh ones, not from cans—and rabbit and deer and even a fish. Or two.

DEME: What do you want?

PAN: I'm talking to the smart one, not the one who asks the same boring questions every day. *(To Romulus:)* Where were you going, and who's there? *(Beat.)* Think of that rabbit, roasted on a spit, with a pinch of... *(To Kali:)* What we got?

KALI: Thyme.

PAN: A pinch of thyme.

DEME: He doesn't know.

PAN: I don't like her voice.

(The Foot Soldiers gag Deme so that she can't talk.)

ROMULUS: If I tell you, I get the rabbit?

PAN: With carrots and potatoes and a pinch of thyme.

SCRUBS: What about me?

ROMULUS: Rabbit gets in my tummy, words might get in my head.

PAN: He *is* the smart one. *(Seductive:)* Give me a few words now, and I'll give you a nice big bite.

ROMULUS: North.

PAN: Give me a word I don't know.

ROMULUS: *(Making it up on the fly:)* There's a man.

PAN: Who is this man?

ROMULUS: A man. With a well.

PAN: There's no wells for 300 miles, maybe 5.

ROMULUS: He's a thousand, up in the mountains. *(Beat.)* C'mon, that's gotta be a bite.

PAN: A man with a mountain well a thousand miles away.

ROMULUS: Yeah. It goes really deep, so there's water for years.

PAN: You're not the smart one.

(She turns to leave.)

ROMULUS: But— Wait!

PAN: Do I look like I'm sleepy?

ROMULUS: No.

PAN: *(Leaving again:)* Then don't tell me bedtime stories.

SCRUBS: They don't know nothing.

PAN: And you do?

SCRUBS: We're goin' north 'cause she got it in her fool head we find the polar bears we're safe.

ROMULUS: Scrubs.

PAN: Polar bears.

SCRUBS: Yep.

ROMULUS: Shut up, Scrubs. *(To Pan:)* She just wants the rabbit.

PAN: Everybody wants the rabbit. *(To Scrubs:)* There are no polar bears here.

SCRUBS: Not here, but maybe there.

PAN: Farther than far. *(To Kali:)* How far?

KALI: Fifteen hundred miles as the crow flies, and that was before. Probably just ghosts now.

PAN: You gonna chase 1500 miles after ghosts? *(Beat.)* So who's the bigger fool: the fool who leads or the fool who follows?

(Scrubs and Romulus are silent.)

(To Kali:) What do you think?

KALI: The fool who follows.

PAN: Reason?

KALI: The fool who follows ought to know better.

PAN: Good. *(To Romulus:)* Don't you worry your pretty face. Tomorrow you'll be 300 miles closer to your polar bear man with a well, and you might even see the sun once a week.

(Pan exits with her entourage. Kali looks back. Beat. She exits. Beat. Deme says something, but we can't understand her through the gag.)

SCRUBS: You know, I kinda like you like this.

(Deme looks viciously at Scrubs, but her words are unintelligible. Romulus looks at the door, then tries to scoot his way toward Deme. While he's doing so:)

What was that thing we found that time? That cartoon. *(Sounding like the teacher in Peanuts:)* Wa-wa-wa-wa-wa-wa. *(Beat.)* That was funny.

(It's going to be an awkward operation, undoing Deme's gag with his own hands that are tied behind his back. There's a SOUND from the door area. Romulus sits where he is, just in time for Kali to return.)

KALI: Don't talk.

(She rips the gag off Deme.)

I only got a couple minutes. In the morning, they're taking you to a water camp in Bend. Old Oregon. Camp's at the bottom of a steep hill, and the truck that's carryin' you can't make it down full of people, and they know it 'cause last month one of 'em near wrecked. So the crew that brought you's gonna drop you, tell the Oregon crew you're there, and split. If they were smart they'd send somebody down the hill, but they don't want to walk it. So you got 15 minutes before the Oregon crew comes up to get you. *(Beat.)* I changed the sheets to say three less. Pan can't read, and the drivers never check, so nobody'll know. *(Produces a key.)* You hide it good and take your shot. If they catch you they'll kill you, so don't get caught.

DEME: Where are the others?

KALI: This way, that way—we've got six water camps and they got gone weeks ago.

DEME: Do you know which—

KALI: You can't help them. You get gone and make for the border crossing at Oroville on old route 97.

ROMULUS: Why are you helping us?

KALI: The fool that follows... *(Beat.)* Your polar bears—they real?

DEME: We hope so.

KALI: I have to go.

ROMULUS: Wait—New San Francisco.

KALI: Someone could come any minute—

ROMULUS: What happened to—

KALI: *(Indicates Deme's mouth:)* Open up.

ROMULUS: There was a girl.

(Kali puts the key in Deme's mouth. Deme closes her mouth.)

KALI: You keep this—

ROMULUS: New San Francisco clothes, but she was coming south when—

KALI: You keep it all the way—

ROMULUS: She's my age.

KALI: Even when you're free, don't toss the key.

ROMULUS: She might be with a kid.

KALI: Nothing was alive on the road. I'm sorry. *(Beat.)* Pan's the big thing down here, but you make it to old Canada, there's powers she won't cross. You make it there fast as you can and then hope like crazy that whatever scares the hell outta Pan likes you more than her.

(She exits, and the lights dim on them.)

SCENE 2

(Kali crosses the stage, and lights come up on her and Pan. It's several days later.)

PAN: Did you think I wouldn't find out about this?

KALI: The runners been skittish since they nearly wrecked.

PAN: Skittish. That a word for lazy?

KALI: Sometimes they do sound the same.

PAN: From now on, two bikes go with the truck. 'Cause of laziness.

KALI: We don't have enough gas.

PAN: Then find some. *(Beat.)* How you reckon those three slipped us?

KALI: Reckon we'll never know.

PAN: Rat said they had a key.

KALI: Rats say what they think will land the cheese.

PAN: Anklets don't fall off by themselves.

KALI: They find a key?

(Pan shakes her head.)

What use is a key once they're done with it?

PAN: Yeah, and...?

KALI: So if they had one, they'd toss it once they used it.

PAN: Then how? *(Beat.)* This does not happen to me!

KALI: We'll find out how.

PAN: People will talk.

KALI: I'll find out how.

PAN: They'll talk and then it'll be back to how it was, scratching for every freaking drop. *(Beat.)* Somebody did this.

KALI: Who reads the magazines to you?

PAN: I don't want to read a magazine.

KALI: Who reads them?

PAN: You do.

KALI: And the books. Who reads you your very favorite book of ever?

PAN: You.

KALI: And who's gonna take care of this and make it go to the neverland?

(Pan smiles, no answer needed. The lights dim on her, and Kali crosses to where a TEEN CAPTIVE, female, sits in front of a makeshift table in a dim room. A pitcher is on the table.)

You're the one that saw.

(The Teen Captive nods.)

Tell me what you saw. *(Beat.)* It's all right. You can tell me. *(Beat.)* I am the right hand of the Pan. Tell me what you saw.

TEEN CAPTIVE: They get us out of the truck. Two girls and a boy, they waited 'til it went down the road, down the hill where nobody could see, then they gave the chains the slip easy as easy can be.

KALI: How'd they do that?

TEEN CAPTIVE: The girl—the bigger one—she has a key. And she does hers and then she does the boy. She does the other girl too, but the other girl has to ask her twice before she does it. The rest want to go. Some of them are begging and yelling for her to unlock them. Not me. I'm loyal. But the rest of them. And then they're gone. Into the woods.

KALI: The three of them.

(The Teen Captive nods.)

With the key.

TEEN CAPTIVE: I guess.

KALI: You guess.

TEEN CAPTIVE: I didn't see it after that. So I guess they took it with.

KALI: *(Beat.)* There was no key.

TEEN CAPTIVE: There was.

KALI: There was no key, because nobody escaped.

TEEN CAPTIVE: But–

KALI: *(Pouring water from the pitcher into a glass:)* Thirsty?

TEEN CAPTIVE: Yes. Please.

(Kali holds out the glass of water but yanks it back when the Teen Captive reaches.)

KALI: You made this up.

TEEN CAPTIVE: No. I didn't make this–

KALI: I think you did.

(Kali pushes the glass of water a few inches in the Teen Captive's direction.)

Because no one gets away from the Pan. *(Beat.)* Can you read and write?

TEEN CAPTIVE: A little.

KALI: Can you sign your name?

(The Teen Captive shakes her head.)

Can you make a mark?

(The Teen Captive nods. Kali pushes the water in front of her and puts a piece of paper and pen alongside it.)

You wanted so badly to show the Pan that you were loyal that you made up the escape. But there were only 14 prisoners on that truck, and every one of them is in the water mines but you.

(Kali holds up the pen to her.)

TEEN CAPTIVE: If I sign the paper...

KALI: You won't have to go down there.

TEEN CAPTIVE: But Pan. She'll be mad if I say I lied.

KALI: There are bad lies, and there are good lies.

TEEN CAPTIVE: She'll punish me.

KALI: This is a good lie.

TEEN CAPTIVE: *(Beat.)* So she won't punish me?

KALI: I promise she won't.

(The Teen Captive signs. The second she finishes, she grabs the water and drinks as if she doesn't know if she'll ever see it again. Kali smiles and pours more water from the pitcher.)

TEEN CAPTIVE: I ain't had this much water in ever.

(She drinks it up, and Kali smiles and refills. She's either enjoying watching the Teen Captive revel in the water, or waiting... Something is not right. The Teen Captive starts to choke. She's been poisoned. She tumbles out of her chair. Clawing for air and Kali:)

You promised...

KALI: It's not a punishment. More like a favor.

(The Teen Captive collapses, dead. End of scene.)

SCENE 3

(Night. Somewhere in what was once northeastern Oregon, close to Washington and Idaho. Romulus is alone, not looking much better than when we saw him last. Enter Cassie. Beat.)

ROMULUS: Cassie? *(Beat.)* I thought you were...

CASSIE: I know.

ROMULUS: But you're not, you're...

CASSIE: I know.

ROMULUS: I'm sorry.

CASSIE: I know you are, Romey.

ROMULUS: We're almost there. We're almost to the border and after that are the white bears and the dancing lights and the clean. Everything will be washed away and we'll be clean.

CASSIE: You go.

ROMULUS: You'll go with me.

CASSIE: I can't.

ROMULUS: I don't want to go without you.

CASSIE: You have to.

ROMULUS: I won't do it again. Not ever.

CASSIE: It's too late. I'm a thousand miles away.

ROMULUS: You're right here.

CASSIE: I'm dead, Romulus.

ROMULUS: No, you—

CASSIE: Nothing to be done.

ROMULUS: We can change it. I can change.

CASSIE: You killed me.

(Cassie's words echo on stage, getting louder and louder as she fades into darkness. Romulus should take his place on the ground, in the middle of a nightmare. Deme leans over him, while Scrubs sits at a distance. They're in a deserted cabin.)

ROMULUS: *(In his sleep:)* Sorry. I'm sorry. Cassie, please... [etc.]

SCRUBS: You gonna shake him before the whole world hears?

DEME: Quiet as quiet can be out there.

SCRUBS: I can be quiet. Don't mean I ain't there.

(Beat. Deme nudges Romulus awake.)

DEME: You were dreamin' again.

SCRUBS: Screamin' more like it. Cassie, I'm sorry. Cassie, please.

DEME: You got anything like a heart in there?

SCRUBS: Ripped it out. Better that way.

ROMULUS: *(Beat.)* I always want to have one. If I don't, just as soon be dead.

SCRUBS: If ya do, gonna get you dead.

ROMULUS: *(Beat.)* You think they're out there?

DEME: Who?

ROMULUS: The people that live here.

SCRUBS: Well they ain't in here.

DEME: You mean are they still...

ROMULUS: Yeah.

DEME: Dunno. But when's the last time you saw somebody past 20?

ROMULUS: They gotta be out there. *(Beat.)* That man. The man from New San Francisco.

SCRUBS: Ghost man.

DEME: Over 12 had to fight.

SCRUBS: 12 to fight to dead.

ROMULUS: I'm makin' it past 20. *(Beat.)* To infinity and beyond! What's that from? I think it's something I heard when I was little. But I don't remember what it was.

(Romulus picks up a coloring book that's been partly colored in.)

They had kids. *(Beat.)* Didn't finish.

(Romulus puts down the book. Scrubs grabs it and looks. Beat.)

SCRUBS: Let's finish it!

ROMULUS: With what?

(Scrubs rummages and finds a trio of crayons.)

SCRUBS: Crayons! I love crayons!

DEME: When you seen a crayon?

SCRUBS: Back in the day. 64 colors Crayola. Built-in sharpener. *(Beat.)* We ain't all fancy pants like you with a TV and books. *(Beat as she starts to color:)* They only got yellow, blue and red.

ROMULUS: Stop.

SCRUBS: I'm just finishing it.

ROMULUS: Don't. *(Beat.)* Someday if they come back, maybe the first thing they'll wanna do is finish coloring, only they'll see it's colored in. And maybe that's all they been thinkin' about the whole time, and we took that away from them.

SCRUBS: Finders keepers.

ROMULUS: I know. But this is different.

(Beat. Scrubs puts down the coloring book. Beat.)

I miss my watch.

DEME: It didn't even work.

ROMULUS: I can still miss it.

SCRUBS: I miss the party pool...and getting in before you!

ROMULUS: Did not!

SCRUBS: Did always! *(Sort of singing:)* Friday night is party night.

(She waits for someone to join in, but nobody does.)

Make the work week come out right. *(Beat.)* Reckon they got the spa? When they got New San Francisco, you think they killed the spa too?

DEME: Scrubs!

SCRUBS: Sorry. Adam said I was trouble with legs. *(Beat.)* Maybe if we don't think so much... *(Beat.)* Ain't nothin' tryin' to dead us this very sec. *(Encouraging:)* Friday night is... Friday night is...

DEME: *(Sort of singing:)* Party night. Make the work week come out right. *(Not singing:)* I can't sing.

SCRUBS: He can't neither.

ROMULUS: I can too. *(Singing:)* Friday night—

ROMULUS, SCRUBS AND DEME: is party night.
Make the work week come out right.

(The conversation stalls.)

SCRUBS: I thought I heard a bird. Day before yesterday.

ROMULUS: Me too.

SCRUBS: Hoot hoot hoot.

ROMULUS: It was caw caw caw.

SCRUBS: Hoot.

ROMULUS: Caw.

(They dance around each other, making rival "hoot" and "caw" sounds.)

DEME: Quiet down.

SCRUBS: Road is still.

ROMULUS: Still still.

DEME: Stop! *(Beat.)* Get some sleep. Gotta make the daylight count.

ROMULUS: You sleep. I had enough dreams tonight.

DEME: You see that dawn start to wake, you shake me.

(Scrubs and Deme settle in to sleep while Romulus watches. Long beat.)

SCRUBS: Maybe I got a little piece, a little piece of heart that I'm savin', hopin' I gotta use for it someday.

ROMULUS: Figured.

SCRUBS: Why ya say that?

ROMULUS: 'Cause you're smart like that.

SCRUBS: Whatever. *(Beat.)* 'Night.

ROMULUS: 'Night.

(The lights dim on them and up on Pan and Kali. They eat from cans of tuna.)

PAN: You ever think what life would be like without tuna?

KALI: There is no tuna. They fished it away.

PAN: But this is tuna.

KALI: And when it runs out, that's that.

(Pan grabs Kali's can.)

PAN: From now on, I get all the tuna.

KALI: *(Beat. Lying:)* I only ate it 'cause you ate it.

PAN: Good girl.

(Kali smiles obediently, then turns away. She's got nothing but hatred on her face.)

You can have anything else.

KALI: Can I have a vegetable?

PAN: Anything you want.

KALI: A fresh one.

PAN: You know who gets the fresh ones.

(Pan pulls out a fresh carrot and starts to eat.)

Take two cans of something. You deserve it.

KALI: The Pan is too generous.

PAN: *(Beat.)* So the rat...

(Kali holds up the signed paper:)

KALI: Says here she made up the whole thing.

PAN: Any chance she might flippity flop?

KALI: No chance.

PAN: Good. Put the word out. *(Beat.)* What?

KALI: We bought a minute. But we both know it happened, and it won't be long before lips get loose and Pan looks weak and slips and falls. Hard.

PAN: They could be anywhere by now.

KALI: They could be, but they're not.

(Beat.)

PAN: Too bad you don't really like tuna. I'd'a opened a can for that.

(The lights dim on them.)

SCENE 4

(Romulus is alone in the light. He sits and wraps his feet.)

ROMULUS: I lost track of how long we've been walking. Every day it's the same. Walk until it blazes high, hide until it starts to slide, walk until it sinks and dies. My feet turned rock, and I don't cry at night anymore. The water we took instead of the coloring book's almost gone, so I don't want to waste it outta my eyes. *(Beat.)* Deme says we're almost there. Maybe one more day. She says that every day. *(Beat.)* Yesterday, there was this lake. The biggest most beautiful lake I've ever seen. Hundreds'a feet around. *(Beat.)* It's almost empty really. If you laid on your back in the middle, it wouldn't even touch your face. *(Beat.)* I just want to wash it off. All the dirt that's stuck on me. And the water isn't deep enough. Maybe if it was deeper I could drown all the wrong and the bad and everything I've done and burst outta the water clean. But it won't come off. No matter how much I rub, it's just caked on me. Like a second skin I can't shed.

(Lights up to reveal Deme and Scrubs. All three are on the road. Deme points forward.)

DEME: It's there.

SCRUBS: Road's the road's the road. Forever and ever.

DEME: No. There.

(A twisted sign says "Canada, 2 miles.")

ROMULUS: Maybe it's just a joke. *(Beat.)* Maybe it's 500 miles.

DEME: Who's gonna carry a sign that says "2 miles" 500 miles just for a joke?

SCRUBS: Don't make no sense, but then again, 'round here got less sense than water.

DEME: Maybe that's gonna change.

SCRUBS: That's a maybe so big I can't lift it.

DEME: It's a beautiful maybe, isn't it, Romey.

ROMULUS: Nothing's beautiful anymore.

DEME: You gotta try to see it.

(Enter Pan, Kali and at least two more BIKERS.)

PAN: We all want things we can't have. Well, not all of us.

DEME: Kali?

PAN: Kali only speaks when I need her to. Isn't that right, Kali?

KALI: Yes.

DEME: We're just three people.

PAN: *(To Kali:)* What was it you said? Lips get loose and...

(Pan gestures to the bikers, who have chains and other makeshift weapons. They start to advance on Romulus, Deme and Scrubs, who draw their own weapons but are outmatched. This won't be pretty.)

KALI: Pan slips...and falls hard.

PAN: That's the part that'll never happen.

(Just when Pan turns her back, Kali stabs her. Pan turns in complete surprise.)

What?!

(Pan sinks to her knees. The Bikers stop, confused. For a moment, we're not sure whose side they'll come down on.)

KALI: Do you want someone who takes all the good food and throws us the scraps? Or what about someone who wastes our precious gas on three people who are going past the end? Or who names herself after a make-believe boy who lives forever and leaves the rest of us to do the dirty work...?

(She's won over the Bikers.)

PAN: *(Dying:)* You...

KALI: You should have given me that tuna.

(Pan is dead. Kali turns her attention to Deme, Romulus and Scrubs, who keep up their guard. We're not clear what's going to happen, but Kali doesn't put away her knife. Beat. The sound of DRUMS, getting louder. Something is coming.)

(Kali signals to the Bikers that they're riding. They exit away from the drums. Deme, Romulus and Scrubs stand back to back to back. As the drums crescendo, a light burns brighter and brighter, eventually becoming almost blinding. Enter KINGUYAKKI, female, Romulus' age, played by the actor who played Cassie.)

ROMULUS: Cassie...?

(Blackout.)

SCENE 5

(Somewhere in western Canada. NANNURALUK, just older than Deme and leader of the First Nations people, stands alone in the light.)

NANNURALUK: I saw one when I was a boy. Before your Southern War turned all the boys into men and the men into ancestors. My father was the greatest of our hunters, and he raised his spear to strike. The path was clear, but in that instant, the spirit of nanuq reached out to my father and made him look into his eyes. There was a conversation that needed no words, my father lowered his spear, and the white bear went north. *(Beat.)* I did not understand. That was our meat and my pants for the coming season, but my father said that I would thank him for making me eat fish and roots and berries from the earth and wear pants that were too short. *(Beat.)* Now I understand.

(The lights come up to reveal Deme standing near him.)

DEME: I should see if he's woken up yet.

NANNURALUK: If not today, then tomorrow.

DEME: I should see.

NANNURALUK: Kinguyakki watches him.

(Lights fade on them and come up on Romulus, lying on a cot and just waking up, confused. Kinguyakki sits by him, watching him. Beat. She holds out a glass of water.)

KINGUYAKKI: It's water.

(Romulus takes it, then smells it before taking a tentative sip and then gulping.)

What did you think it was?

ROMULUS: Dunno. *(Beat.)* Where are we?

KINGUYAKKI: Our land.

(Beat. Romulus waits for more information.)

The people of the First Nations. You crossed into our lands a week ago.

ROMULUS: A week? Have I been— Where's my sister?

KINGUYAKKI: With my brother. *(Beat.)* Who's Cassie?

ROMULUS: *(Beat.)* I let her go.

KINGUYAKKI: Then it's done.

ROMULUS: It's not done. It feels like it'll never be done.

KINGUYAKKI: Far worse things have been done in one wink of the universe.

ROMULUS: Not by me.

KINGUYAKKI: You didn't drive her out.

ROMULUS: How do you know?

KINGUYAKKI: I know you.

ROMULUS: How?

KINGUYAKKI: For a week I watched you sleep.

ROMULUS: I sleep but I wake like it never was. There's never any peace, 'cause it's always her voice: Coward. Coward.

KINGUYAKKI: That's how I know you are good—

ROMULUS: I am not good.

KINGUYAKKI: Because the demons won't leave you alone.

ROMULUS: I don't believe in demons.

KINGUYAKKI: There are all kinds of demons. The ones in the spirit world and the ones we make ourselves.

(The light dims on them and up on Deme and Nannuraluk.)

NANNURALUK: Do not worry. He is safe with her.

DEME: Is *she* safe?

NANNURALUK: Ugalik keeps watch.

DEME: I hope that's a warrior.

NANNURALUK: He is many things.

(The lights dim on them and come up on Scrubs, in a third area of the stage. She's exploring. UGALIK, both impish and wise beyond his years and played by the actor who played Echo, growls like a wolf from offstage. Scrubs jumps for a moment. Beat. Ugalik growls again and maybe even howls.)

SCRUBS: Dunno what you are, but scary you ain't.

(Ugalik growls and howls again. This time, Scrubs yawns and makes as if to go to sleep, closing her eyes. Beat. Enter Ugalik wearing a wolf mask.)

UGALIK: You were too scared.

SCRUBS: I look scared?

UGALIK: You jumped.

SCRUBS: Movin' ain't jumpin'. *(Beat.)* I had an itch.

UGALIK: Did not. I got you good.

(Scrubs opens her eyes as she senses him moving closer. She sees him and his mask.)

SCRUBS: You're nothin' but a little bit.

UGALIK: Hey—I'm getting bigger.

SCRUBS: Lil Bit. That's what I'm namin' you.

UGALIK: My name is Ugalik.

SCRUBS: Lil Bit's gonna stick in my head.

UGALIK: It's not my name.

SCRUBS: Lil Wolf. Lil somethin'.

UGALIK: *(Removing his mask:)* Ugalik.

(Scrubs sees his face and jumps.)

SCRUBS: Stay away, ghost!

UGALIK: Ghost?

SCRUBS: *(Scooting away:)* Just stay put.

(Ugalik growls again.)

UGALIK: Scared you now.

(The lights dim on them and return to Deme and Nannuraluk.)

DEME: Many things?

NANNURALUK: Many.

DEME: Good ones?

NANNURALUK: Mostly.

DEME: *(Beat.)* We can work for supplies.

NANNURALUK: *(Shaking his head:)* You are our guests.

DEME: People don't just give–

NANNURALUK: Why not?

DEME: *(Beat.)* It's not the world we're used to.

NANNURALUK: It should be.

DEME: *(Beat.)* How do– Why don't– Why did they just leave when you came?

NANNURALUK: The new world lives on the edge of the end, but even now the earth gives power to those who always loved it.

DEME: They'll come back.

NANNURALUK: We lead lives of peace until it is time not to.

DEME: They'll come here.

NANNURALUK: Your friends to the south know this. They have been taught.

DEME: Once my brother is better, just give us what you can.

NANNURALUK: Take what you think you need. But it is not what he needs.

(As the lights fade on them, they come back to Scrubs and Ugalik:)

UGALIK: Don't be scared.

SCRUBS: Ain't. Just you stay put.

UGALIK: Wanna see my mask? I made it.

SCRUBS: You made it?

UGALIK: All by myself. *(Beat.)* I'm not a ghost. *(Beat.)* I can talk to spirits. Or I will when I get older.

SCRUBS: What kind of spirits?

UGALIK: Animals. People. Now I can only listen.

SCRUBS: What they say?

UGALIK: *(Trying to sound like different animals:)* Woosh... Howl... Grrr...

SCRUBS: That don't sound like talk.

UGALIK: *(As Echo:)* Don't f-f-feel b-bad.

SCRUBS: *(Jarred by the familiarity:)* What?!

UGALIK: *(Still as Echo:)* I am one with the white bear.

SCRUBS: One with— You're—

(The spirit has left Ugalik, and he has no idea it happened.)

UGALIK: I'm what?

SCRUBS: You said you were one with the white bear.

UGALIK: No I didn't.

SCRUBS: Came out of your mouth.

UGALIK: *(Summons a wad of spit:)* This comes out of my mouth.

SCRUBS: *(Summons her own spit:)* Yeah, well I got more.

UGALIK: *(Holding the spit in his mouth:)* No you don't.

SCRUBS: Do.

UGALIK: Don't.

(Enter Kinguyakki.)

KINGUYAKKI: *(To Ugalik:)* We need you.

UGALIK: When I come back, wanna go fishing?

SCRUBS: What's fishing?

UGALIK: We look for fish.

SCRUBS: In the can?

UGALIK: In the water, silly.

SCRUBS: How?

UGALIK: Fishing's the best.

(He exits.)

SCRUBS: Fishing.

(The lights dim on her and give way to INUIT RITUAL DRUMMING, which should get louder and louder in the darkness. The stage could stay in darkness with percussion only, or a more ambitious production could let the initial darkness – allowing for a costume change – give way to an Inuit dance sequence, led by Ugalik, now attired as a shaman. At the end, the DRUMS crescendo, with blinding light, then blackness and finally coming up for the next scene.)

SCENE 6

(Near the hot springs. An upstage platform, perhaps with a ladder descending to the hot spring that we never see, might serve as the gateway. Deme, now dressed in Inuit garb, waits anxiously, with Kinguyakki, Nannuraluk, Scrubs, also dressed in Inuit garb, and perhaps other members of the tribe nearby. Romulus, stripped for bathing, emerges from an unseen hot spring. He is soaking wet. Kinguyakki wraps him in a blanket.)

SCRUBS: So what happened? What did he say?

ROMULUS: Can I get dry first?

SCRUBS: Just tell me—was it better than the party pool?

ROMULUS: Like the party pool with bubbles.

SCRUBS: That's all?

ROMULUS: *(Shakes his head:)* The water comes down like rain.

SCRUBS: Ain't never felt rain.

ROMULUS: Me neither. But I used to dream about it when I was little. And it was just like that.

SCRUBS: *(Beat.)* And then what?

DEME: Scrubs, leave it.

SCRUBS: C'mon—just quick say what happened!

ROMULUS: I don't know.

SCRUBS: You were there, weren't you?

(Ugalik emerges, dressed as a shaman, though he's getting out of his costume in the same way that a kid who's been forced into a suit gets it off the second he's allowed. Members of the Inuit ensemble treat his costume with reverence, collecting everything as he sheds it. Scrubs makes a beeline for him. To Ugalik:)

First you spill the story, then we do the fishing thing.

DEME: You OK?

ROMULUS: Wet.

DEME: Good to feel wet after all that dry.

(Kinguyakki approaches them. To Romulus:)

KINGUYAKKI: I have new clothes for you.

ROMULUS: What happened to my–

DEME: You're lucky that they didn't fall off before we got here.

ROMULUS: *(Taking them:)* Thank you.

DEME: They're solid. Good for the road.

ROMULUS: *(Beat.)* I think we should stay.

DEME: *(Beat.)* You know we can't do that.

ROMULUS: Why not?

DEME: We are so close, Romey. *(Beat.)* Nannurulak has seen them.

ROMULUS: When?

DEME: They might be just a few days away.

ROMULUS: When did he see them?

DEME: You know it won't last here. New San Francisco was supposed to last and now it's ash.

ROMULUS: We don't know where they are.

UGALIK: *(As Echo:)* The white bears live forever in the land of 60 degrees north, 135 degrees west, and the Aurora Borealis dances with joy above their heads.

DEME: *(Beat.)* When we get there, I promise we can—

ROMULUS: What? Stop?

DEME: They will be there.

ROMULUS: I'm not like you.

DEME: You're my brother.

ROMULUS: You love the road.

DEME: It's all there is.

ROMULUS: I don't believe that anymore.

DEME: *(Beat. Indicating the spring:)* What happened there?

ROMULUS: I don't know. Ugalik said some words I couldn't understand and the drummers drummed and the water rained and I just wanted to stay a part of it.

(Scrubs returns from her conversation with Ugalik, who exits in search of fishing poles.)

DEME: *(Beat.)* You'd let me go into the nowhere.

ROMULUS: Adam and Eve, Cassie,

SCRUBS: Echo...

ROMULUS: You... People leave. They do what's inside them to do, and I can't carry that.

DEME: We're leaving tomorrow.

ROMULUS: Then you are.

DEME: That play you were always sneak reading.

ROMULUS: How'd you know about—

DEME: You really think you could hide it—

ROMULUS: Did you read it?

DEME: All but the end. It's the play Mom and Dad saw.

ROMULUS: Nobody knows the end.

DEME: He comes.

ROMULUS: How do you know? Did they tell you?

DEME: He's got to. Or else why do it?

ROMULUS: What if he doesn't? What if it's just up to them to stop?

DEME: *(Beat.)* It won't last. Here is like ever.

ROMULUS: Maybe it will.

DEME: And if not?

ROMULUS: Then I'll do what needs doin'.

SCRUBS: *(Beat.)* I wanna try this fishing thing before we go. I ain't never done it, and I figure I better cross it off the list now, in case there ain't no fish on the road.

ROMULUS: *(To Scrubs:)* Thank you.

SCRUBS: You gone all screwy since you been in that...is it better than the spa?

> *(Romulus smiles and nods. Enter Ugalik with two fishing poles. He puts one in Scrubs' hands and runs off. The lights fade on all but Scrubs.)*

Wish somebody showed me fishin' when I was tiny, 'cause I taken to it like dust to a shoe. 'Course, it helps there being fish. *(Beat.)* Way I see it, it's a game of who blinks first: you or the fish. And I might just be the best there ever was, except for Ugalik. He's givin' me a rod, in case we run into more fish up north. Deme won't believe it 'til she sees—maybe not even then. *(Beat.)* But I think I was born to do it. Just took me a spell to find out. Wish where we belonged would reach out and slap us in the face and say, "You're here." Well maybe not slap. You know what I mean. But guess sometimes you just gotta come to it. Like a fish and a line.

SCENE 7

(The lights gradually come up on the rest of the stage.)

(Enter Deme, who puts a pack into Scrubs' hands. Scrubs, holding her fishing pole, occupies herself with that and her pack, giving Deme a moment alone with Romulus. Kinguyakki is on stage but gives them their space.)

DEME: *(Pulling out Romulus' watch:)* I've been holding onto this forever.

ROMULUS: My watch.

(She gives it to him.)

DEME: It still doesn't work.

(Beat.)

ROMULUS: *(Holding it out to her:)* Here.

DEME: It's your watch.

ROMULUS: I know. But you might need it.

DEME: A broken watch.

ROMULUS: Maybe the polar bears got batteries.

DEME: Yeah. Baskets of batteries they keep in their snow houses.

ROMULUS: I just thought maybe you'd want to have it...'cause it was mine.

DEME: I don't need a watch for that.

ROMULUS: I know. But still.

(They embrace for a long time. Scrubs, finished with her pack, waits impatiently.)

SCRUBS: You gonna mush it up forever?

ROMULUS: *(Breaking the embrace:)* Scrubs.

SCRUBS: You try it on me I'll—

ROMULUS: You'll what.

SCRUBS: Just don't.

(Romulus grabs her before she can get away and hugs her.)

Off off off.

(Romulus lets her go.)

ROMULUS: Gotcha.

DEME: *(Beat.)* North.

(Deme and Scrubs exit. Beat.)

ROMULUS: You mind if we just stand here for a minute?

KINGUYAKKI: We've got time.

(Beat. He takes her hand. The Aurora Borealis begins to dance. Blackout and end of play.)

The Author Speaks

What inspired you to write this play?

The image of the polar bear has been emblematic of climate change—we often hear stories of their shrinking habitat and how the loss of ice is affecting their ability to feed. They are these beautiful and majestic white bears—admittedly, not as cuddly as they look unless they're in stuffed animal form—and that beauty makes for a compelling, iconic image, something that is always important to me when it comes to creating a play. ***Rumors of Polar Bears*** began as a one-act (which is separately published by another company), but I always planned for it to be a three-act cycle, and with this version, that has now come to fruition. And, quite frankly, I wanted to write a play with a kiddie pool in it.

Was the structure or other elements of the play influenced by any other work?

Originally, I intended the structure of the play to resemble ***Gunplay***, a play cycle I wrote roughly twenty years before (wow—I feel old!), which had three stand-alone one-acts. But as I continued to work on it, I realized that while the first act (now named "Oil and Water") can stand on its own, the second ("Ursa Major") and third ("Northern Lights") acts of the cycle are too intertwined with everything else that comes before and after to truly stand on their own. Ultimately, it requires the full play for the arcs of Deme, Romulus and Scrubs to unfold, and so it just doesn't make sense to do only the second or third acts.

Structurally, ***Rumors of Polar Bears*** is a sweeping road epic (***Milk and Cookies*** and ***Beef Junkies*** are road plays, but not nearly of this scope), which makes it fairly unique in my current catalogue, but its often cinematic nature has commonalities with much of my recent work (for example, plays like ***The Locker Next 2 Mine*** and even the comedic ***Harry's Hotter at Twilight*** tend to jump from place to place cinematically with suggested settings in the same way). Further, my YouthPLAYS co-founder Ed Shockley and I have talked about how the monologue in many ways has become an endangered species in contemporary theatre, but I still love writing them, and you'll see quite a few here, just as there are in ***Locker...*** and numerous others of my plays. To me, monologues are a valuable way to change the play's rhythm (I think of plays as pieces of music), and they give a play "size," allowing characters to lead audiences to new worlds. They're also useful for auditions and classroom use, though that's not why I write them. Finally, I love creating "choral" moments for ensembles, and you'll see a few of them here, notably in New San Francisco and among Mrs. Middleton's Former Pre-Kindergarten Drama Class.

Have you dealt with the same theme in other works that you have written?

On the surface, people may think that ***Rumors of Polar Bears*** is about climate change. It's not that it doesn't address the issue, and it's not that I don't think it's important. Of course it is, and without being preachy, I hope that the play illustrates what may happen if we're not better stewards of our finite resources, an issue I dealt with in the darkly comic ***Beef Junkies***. But ultimately ***Rumors of Polar Bears*** is a play about family, exploring both the nature of family and of the bonds that tie us to other people. When I go back through my collected works, another play that explores these same issues is ***Ben***, about a homeless teen looking for the woman he thinks is his mother—and the surrogate father he finds in a restaurant owner. The play also explores the lengths to which we'll go to chase a dream, which is a further examination of issues present in ***4 A.M.***, which looks at the balance between our dreams and our fears as we press forward.

What do you hope to achieve with this work?

I started writing for teens... Well, let's be honest: I started doing it because I got paid to write some plays for them, but I've grown to love writing for this age group, because at their best, they are energetic and curious and will fearlessly dive off whatever cliff you lead them to. Not enough opportunities exist, however—and it's part of the reason Ed Shockley and I founded YouthPLAYS—for young people to play characters their own age. I doubt that many teens see a bit of themselves in Willy Loman, but I'm hoping that in the struggles of people like Deme, Romulus, Scrubs or Cassie they may, and that in not having to focus on walking like 65-year-old men, they can focus on giving the kind of powerful, truthful performances of which they are capable.

What were the biggest challenges involved in the writing of this play?

I went on a roughly three-year hiatus from when I wrote the one-act version of the play to when I started up again working on the remaining two parts of the cycle. I wrote perhaps four pages somewhere in between, and for several years, I'd carry along these pages on trips, vainly hoping I'd get more work done on the rest. Somehow, in late 2013, I decided that enough was enough and plunged back in. I find starting any new play to be slightly terrifying—what if it's not any good when it hits the paper?—but it's particularly challenging to return to a play after a long hiatus. You're not quite the same person you were, and finding the flow and hearing the characters' voices again can be difficult. But I think that the break turned out to be useful, and it's allowed me to polish some things in the first part of the cycle. The other challenge was that this was unlike anything I'd written in terms of its scope, and that created pressure not to "write small."

What are the most common mistakes that occur in productions of your work?

Because I write so cinematically, there's a tendency for productions to want to put in blackouts, but blackouts are a pace killer, so to the extent that you can, try to avoid them. I'd rather see a very theatrical play with the actors self-consciously on stage than a very naturalistic production that ends up needing giant blackouts to move things and people around. The other thing is that a play can be about a serious topic without being one long dirge. Yes, there may be serious moments that need to be played straight, but I love leavening seriousness with comedy—I find that it's often an easier entrance point for a tough subject—and it's OK to be funny and to keep the pacing up. Both ***Rumors of Polar Bears*** and ***The Locker Next 2 Mine*** are about serious subjects, but both contain plenty of comedy. Don't be afraid to embrace that humor, as the contrast helps give the play texture. Trust that the writing will take care of delivering the dramatic payload where needed—just play your given circumstances as honestly as you can.

How did you research the subject?

In terms of the climate change backdrop, years of reading the newspaper every morning and living in Southern California, where we are constantly suffering through drought and wildfires, supplemented by some strategic research on climate issues, has helped. Things like the rising of sea levels, squabbles over the Colorado River aquifer, the northward creep of tropical diseases are all amped up versions of things that have actually happened. When it came to the Inuit names, I got help from Dr. Lawrence Kaplan of the Alaska Native

Language Center at the University of Alaska-Fairbanks. The location of the Inuits, which is meant to be somewhere in western Canada, is something of a hybrid, as it needed to be a place with a good view of the Aurora Borealis, as well as one that had hot springs. Of course, there were other bits of research, such as finding piano pieces that would have been appropriate for Noah to play as a small child (though he's a prodigy, so it was fine for the pieces to be complex), but much of the play comes from my own head and my general knowledge.

Shakespeare gave advice to the players in *Hamlet*; if you could give advice to your cast what would it be?
Dive headfirst into the world of the play, and don't be afraid to take risks and make strong choices. Hopefully, it's a different one from any world in which you will ever live. The play has plenty of humor, and don't shy away from it—embrace it and have fun with it. And don't wear really nice footwear. Nobody's going to have new sneakers after the Oil and Water Wars.

About the Author

Jonathan Dorf is a Los Angeles-based playwright, screenwriter, teacher and script consultant, whose plays have been produced in nearly every state in the US, as well as in Canada, Europe, Asia, Africa, Central America, Australia, and New Zealand. He is Co-Chair of the Alliance of Los Angeles Playwrights and the Resident Playwriting Expert for Final Draft and The Writers Store. He directed the theatre program at The Haverford School and spent three years at Choate Rosemary Hall Summer Arts Conservatory as playwright-in-residence. A frequent guest artist at Thespian conferences and schools, he has served as Visiting Professor of Theatre in the

MFA Playwriting and Children's Literature programs at Hollins University, and as United States cultural envoy to Barbados. He holds a BA in Dramatic Writing and Literature from Harvard College and an MFA in Playwriting from UCLA. He is a member of The Dramatists Guild and a life member of the Philadelphia Dramatists Center. Website: http://jonathandorf.com.

About YouthPLAYS

YouthPLAYS (www.youthplays.com) is a publisher of award-winning professional dramatists and talented new discoveries, each with an original theatrical voice, and all dedicated to expanding the vocabulary of theatre for young actors and audiences. On our website you'll find one-act and full-length plays and musicals for teen and pre-teen (and even college) actors, as well as duets and monologues for competition. Many of our authors' works have been widely produced at high schools and middle schools, youth theatres and other TYA companies, both amateur and professional, as well as at elementary schools, camps, churches and other institutions serving young audiences and/or actors worldwide. Most are intended for performance by young people, while some are intended for adult actors performing for young audiences.

YouthPLAYS was co-founded by professional playwrights Jonathan Dorf and Ed Shockley. It began merely as an additional outlet to market their own works, which included a substantial body of award-winning published and unpublished plays and musicals. Those interested in their published plays were directed to the respective publishers' websites, and unpublished plays were made available in electronic form. But when they saw the desperate need for material for young actors and audiences—coupled with their experience that numerous quality plays for young people weren't finding a home—they made the decision to represent the work of other playwrights as well. Dozens and dozens of authors are now members of the YouthPLAYS family, with scripts available both electronically and in traditional acting editions. We continue to grow as we look for exciting and challenging plays and musicals for young actors and audiences.

About ProduceaPlay.com

Let's put up a play! Great idea! But producing a play takes time, energy and knowledge. While finding the necessary time and energy is up to you, ProduceaPlay.com is a website designed to assist you with that third element: knowledge.

Created by YouthPLAYS' co-founders, Jonathan Dorf and Ed Shockley, ProduceaPlay.com serves as a resource for producers at all levels as it addresses the many facets of production. As Dorf and Shockley speak from their years of experience (as playwrights, producers, directors and more), they are joined by a group of award-winning theatre professionals and experienced teachers from the world of academic theatre, all making their expertise available for free in the hope of helping this and future generations of producers, whether it's at the school or university level, or in community or professional theatres.

The site is organized into a series of major topics, each of which has its own page that delves into the subject in detail, offering suggestions and links for further information. For example, Publicity covers everything from Publicizing Auditions to How to Use Social Media to Posters to whether it's worth hiring a publicist. Casting details Where to Find the Actors, How to Evaluate a Resume, Callbacks and even Dealing with Problem Actors. You'll find guidance on your Production Timeline, The Theater Space, Picking a Play, Budget, Contracts, Rehearsing the Play, The Program, House Management, Backstage, and many other important subjects.

The site is constantly under construction, so visit often for the latest insights on play producing, and let it help make your play production dreams a reality.

More from YouthPLAYS

The Locker Next 2 Mine by Jonathan Dorf
Dramedy. 80-85 minutes. 5-12+ males, 8-16+ females (14-40 performers possible).

Alisa arrives at a new high school in the middle of the year to find her locker next to a shrine for a popular lacrosse player who's died in an auto accident, but as she digs deeper, she discovers another death that no one talks about, even as it's left many of the school's students trying to pick up their own pieces. A play about teen suicide and dealing with loss.

The Legend of Sleepy Hollow by Jonathan Josephson
Adaptation. 25-30 minutes. 4+ males, 1+ females, 4+ either (5-15 performers possible).

A theatrical adaptation of Washington Irving's timeless tale of Ichabod Crane, the fair damsel Katrina Van Tassel, and the most feared spectre of the realm, the Headless Horseman of Sleepy Hollow. An ideal Halloween story that's a pleasure all year long for lovers of literature and theatre!

The Old New Kid by Adam J. Goldberg
Comedy. 30-40 minutes. 2-9+ males, 3-10+ females (8-30+ performers possible).

It's the half-day of school before Thanksgiving break, and current "new kid" Alan Socrates Bama just wants to get through the day. But when a new-new kid arrives, things change. Alan has three hours to find the meaning of Thanksgiving, survive elementary school politics, battle for his identity, and spell the word "cornucopia" in this *Peanuts*-flavored comedy for kids of all ages.

Jennifer the Unspecial: Time Travel, Love Potions & 8th Grade by Matthew Mezzacappa (book & lyrics) & Cynthia Chi-Wing Wong (music)
Musical. 90 minutes. 5-30 males, 3-30 females (8-60 performers possible).

When her science teacher's invention goes horribly wrong, awkward, clumsy eighth grader Jennifer finds herself thrust into a time-traveling adventure with three of her classmates. Through the journey, as they encounter warriors, artists, presidents and love potions, Jennifer discovers she doesn't need anyone's approval to be absolutely amazing and special.

Gwen and Mary at Glenn Ross by Robin Pond
Comedy. 54-64 minutes. 7 either.

Mamet's classic tale of cutthroat real estate salesmen gets a darkly comic reboot in this parody that goes back to the source, Glenn Ross Academy, a private school for pre-teen overachievers. As students fight for their place on "the Board" amid peer pressure and stratospheric family expectations, they learn to do whatever it takes to compete. And if the constant manipulation and shifting alliances weren't enough, just wait until the questions to an all-important standardized test go missing and the finger pointing begins...

The Mystic Tale of Aladdin by Randy Wyatt
Fantasy. 50-60 minutes. 9 females.

Seven princesses wait to hear which of them the Sultan has chosen for his bride. To pass the final minutes before he announces his decision, the maidens tell the tale of Aladdin, a tale each claims as her country's own. Filled with magic, adventure, intrigue and romance, this all-female version of the classic story packs a powerful message of empowering young women to fulfill their own wishes.